Machine L(For Absolute Beginners: A Plain English Introduction

Hilda Beaman

Third Edition
Copyright © 2021

For feedback, print quality issues, media contact, omissions or errors regarding this book, please contact

TABLE OF CONTENTS

## 1

PREFACE

Machines have come a long way since the onset of the Industrial Revolution. They continue to fill factory floors and manufacturing plants, but their capabilities extend beyond manual activities to cognitive tasks that, until recently, only humans were capable of performing. Judging song contests, driving automobiles, and detecting fraudulent transactions are three examples of the complex tasks machines are now capable of simulating.

But these remarkable feats trigger fear among some observers. Part of their fear nestles on the neck of survivalist insecurities and provokes the deep-seated question of *what if*? *What if* intelligent machines turn on us in a struggle of the fittest? *What if* intelligent machines produce offspring with capabilities that humans never intended to impart to machines? *What if* the legend of the *singularity* is true?

The other notable fear is the threat to job security, and if you're a taxi driver or an accountant, there's a valid reason to be worried. According to joint research from the Office for National Statistics and Deloitte UK published by the BBC in 2015, job professions including bar worker (77%), waiter (90%), chartered accountant (95%), receptionist (96%), and taxi driver (57%) have a high chance of being automated by the year 2035.[1] Nevertheless, research on planned job automation and crystal ball gazing concerning the future evolution of machines and artificial intelligence (AI) should be read with a pinch of skepticism. In *Superintelligence: Paths, Dangers, Strategies*, author Nick Bostrom discusses the continuous redeployment of AI goals and how "two decades is a sweet spot…near enough to be attention-grabbing and relevant, yet far enough to make it possible that a string of breakthroughs…might by then have occurred."([2])([3])

While AI is moving fast, broad adoption remains an unchartered path fraught with known and unforeseen challenges. Delays and other obstacles are inevitable. Nor is machine learning a simple case of flicking a switch and asking the machine to predict the outcome of the Super Bowl and serve you a delicious martini.

Far from a typical out-of-the-box analytics solution, machine learning relies on statistical algorithms managed and overseen by skilled individuals called data scientists and machine learning engineers. This is one labor market where job opportunities are destined to grow but where supply is struggling to meet demand.

In fact, the current shortage of professionals with the necessary expertise and training is one of the primary obstacles delaying AI's progress. According, the Director of Thought Leadership at Belatrix Software:

"It's a huge challenge to find data scientists, people with machine learning

experience, or people with the skills to analyze and use the data, as well as those who can create the algorithms required for machine learning. Secondly, while the technology is still emerging, there are many ongoing developments. It's clear that AI is a long way from how we might imagine it."[4]

Perhaps your own path to working in the field of machine learning starts here, or maybe a baseline understanding is sufficient to fulfill your curiosity for now.

This book focuses on the high-level fundamentals, including key terms, general workflow, and the statistical underpinnings of basic algorithms to set you on your path. To design and code intelligent machines, you'll first need to develop a strong grasp of classical statistics. Algorithms derived from classical statistics sit at the core of machine learning and constitute the metaphorical neurons and nerves that power artificial cognitive abilities. Coding is the other indispensable part of machine learning, which includes managing and manipulating large amounts of data.

Unlike building a web 2.0 landing page with click-and-drag tools like Wix and WordPress, machine learning requires Python, C++, R or another programming language. If you haven't learned a relevant programming language, you will need to if you wish to make further progress in this field. But for the purpose of this compact starter's course, the following chapters can be completed without any programming experience.

While this book serves as an introductory course to machine learning, please note that it does not constitute an absolute beginner's introduction to mathematics, computer programming, and statistics. A cursory knowledge of these fields or convenient access to an Internet connection may be required to aid understanding in later chapters.

For those who wish to dive into the coding aspect of machine learning, Chapter 17 and Chapter 18 walk you through the entire process of setting up a machine learning model using Python. A gentle introduction to coding with Python has also been included in the Appendix and information regarding further learning resources can be found in the final section of is book.

## 2

WHAT IS MACHINE LEARNING?

In 1959, IBM published a paper in the *IBM Journal of Research and Development* with an intriguing and obscure title. Authored by IBM's Arthur Samuel, the paper investigated the application of machine learning in the game of checkers "to verify the fact that a computer can be programmed so that it will learn to play a better game of checkers than can be played by the person who wrote the program." [5]

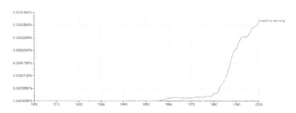

Figure 1: Historical mentions of "machine learning" in published books. *Source: Google Ngram Viewer, 2017*

Although it wasn't the first published paper to use the term "machine learning" per se, Arthur Samuel is regarded as the first person to coin and define machine learning as the concept and specialized field we know today. Samuel's landmark journal submission, *Some Studies in Machine Learning Using the Game of Checkers,* introduced machine learning as a subfield of computer science that gives computers the ability to learn without being explicitly programmed.

While not directly treated in Arthur Samuel's initial definition, a key characteristic of machine learning is the concept of *self-learning.* This refers to the application of statistical modeling to detect patterns and improve performance based on data and empirical information;

all without direct programming commands. This is what Arthur Samuel described as the ability to learn without being explicitly programmed. Samuel didn't infer that machines may formulate decisions with no upfront programming. On the contrary, machine learning is heavily dependent on code input. Instead, he observed machines can perform a set task using *input data* rather than relying on a direct *input command*.

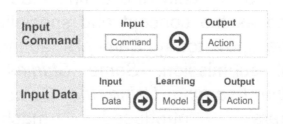

Figure 2: Comparison of Input Command vs Input Data

An example of an input command is entering "2+2" in a programming language such as Python and clicking "Run" or hitting "Enter" to view the output.
>>> 2+2
4
>>>

This represents a direct command with a pre-programmed answer, which is typical of most computer applications. Unlike traditional computer programming, though, where outputs or decisions are pre-defined by the programmer, machine learning uses data as input to build a decision model. Decisions are generated by deciphering relationships and patterns in the data using probabilistic reasoning, trial and error, and other computationally-intensive techniques. This means that the output of the decision model is determined by the contents of the input data rather than any pre-set rules defined by a human programmer. The human programmer is still responsible for feeding the data into the model, selecting an appropriate algorithm and tweaking its settings (called *hyperparameters*) in a bid to reduce prediction error, but ultimately the machine and developer operate a layer apart in contrast to traditional programming.

To draw an example, let's suppose that after analyzing YouTube viewing habits, the decision model identifies a significant relationship among data scientists who like watching cat videos. A separate model, meanwhile, identifies patterns among the physical traits of baseball players and their likelihood of winning the season's Most Valuable Player (MVP) award.

In the first scenario, the machine analyzes which videos data scientists enjoy watching on YouTube based on user engagement; measured in likes, subscribes, and repeat viewing. In the second scenario, the machine assesses the physical attributes of previous baseball MVPs among other features such as age and education. However, at no stage was the decision model told or programmed to produce those two outcomes. By decoding complex patterns in the input data, the model uses machine learning to find connections without human help. This also means that a related dataset collected from another time period, with fewer or greater data points, might push the model to produce a slightly different output.

Another distinct feature of machine learning is the ability to improve predictions based on experience. Mimicking the way humans base decisions on experience and the success or failure of past attempts, machine learning utilizes exposure to data to improve its decision making. The socializing of data points provides experience and enables the model to familiarize itself with patterns in the data. Conversely, insufficient input data restricts the model's ability to deconstruct underlying patterns in the data and limits its capacity to respond to potential variance and random phenomena found in live data. Exposure to input data thereby deepens the model's understanding of patterns, including the significance of changes in the data, and to construct an effective self-learning model.

A common example of a self-learning model is a system for detecting spam email messages. Following an initial serving of input data, the model learns to flag emails with suspicious subject lines and body text containing keywords that correlate strongly with spam messages flagged by users in the past. Indications of spam email may include words like *dear friend, free, invoice, PayPal, Viagra, casino, payment, bankruptcy,* and *winner.* However, as more data is analyzed, the model might also find exceptions and incorrect assumptions that render the model susceptible to bad predictions. If there is limited data to reference its decision, the following email subject, for example, might be wrongly classified as spam: "**PayPal** has received your **payment** for **Casino** Royale purchased on eBay."

As this is a genuine email sent from a PayPal auto-responder, the spam detection system is lured into producing a false-positive based on previous input data. Traditional programming is highly susceptible to this problem because the model is rigidly defined according to pre-set rules. Machine learning, on the other hand, emphasizes exposure to data as a way to refine the model, adjust weak assumptions, and respond appropriately to unique data points such as the scenario just described.

While data is used to source the self-learning process, more data doesn't always equate to better decisions; the input data must be relevant. In *Data and Goliath: The Hidden Battles to Collect Your Data and Control Your World,* Bruce Schneir writes that, "When looking for the needle, the last thing you want to do is pile lots more hay on it."[6] This means that adding irrelevant data can be counter-productive to achieving a desired result. In addition, the amount of input data should be compatible with the processing resources and time that is available.

Training & Test Data

In machine learning, the input data is typically split into *training data* and *test data*. The first split of data is the *training data*, which is the initial reserve of data used to develop the model. In the spam email detection example, false-positives similar to the PayPal auto-response message might be detected from the training data. Modifications must then be made to the model, e.g., email notifications issued from the sending address "payments@paypal.com" should be excluded from spam filtering. Using machine learning, the model can be trained to automatically detect these errors (by analyzing historical examples of spam messages and deciphering their patterns) without direct human interference.

After you have developed a model based on patterns extracted from the training data and you are satisfied with the accuracy of its predictions, you can test the model on the remaining data, known as the *test data*. If you are also satisfied with the model's performance using the test data, the model is ready to filter incoming emails in a live setting and generate decisions on how to categorize those messages. We will discuss training and test data further in Chapter 6.

The Anatomy of Machine Learning

The final section of this chapter explains how machine learning fits into the broader landscape of data science and computer science. This includes understanding how machine learning connects with parent fields and sister disciplines. This is important, as you will encounter related terms in machine learning literature and courses. Relevant disciplines can also be difficult to tell apart, especially machine learning and data mining.

Let's start with a high-level introduction. Machine learning, data mining, artificial intelligence, and computer programming all fall under the umbrella of computer science, which encompasses everything related to the design and use of computers. Within the all-encompassing space of computer science is the next broad field of data science. Narrower than computer science, data science comprises methods and systems to extract knowledge and insights from data with the aid of computers.

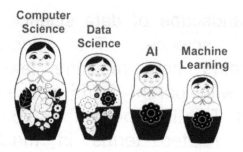

Figure 3: The lineage of machine learning represented by a row of Russian matryoshka dolls

Emerging from computer science and data science as the third matryoshka doll from the left in Figure 3 is artificial intelligence. Artificial intelligence, or AI, encompasses the ability of machines to perform intelligent and cognitive tasks. Comparable to how the Industrial Revolution gave birth to an era of machines simulating physical tasks, AI is driving the development of machines capable of simulating cognitive abilities.

While still broad but dramatically more honed than computer science and data science, AI spans numerous subfields that are popular and newsworthy today. These subfields include search and planning, reasoning and knowledge representation, perception, natural language processing (NLP), and of course, machine learning.

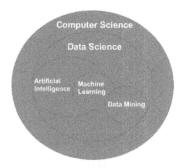

Figure 4: Visual representation of the relationship between data-related fields

For students interested in AI, machine learning provides an excellent starting point as it provides a narrower and more practical lens of study (in comparison to AI). Algorithms applied in machine learning can also be used in other disciplines, including perception and natural language processing. In addition, a Master's degree is adequate to develop a certain level of expertise in machine learning, but you may need a PhD to make genuine progress in the field of artificial intelligence.

As mentioned, machine learning overlaps with data mining—a sister discipline based on discovering and unearthing patterns in large datasets. Both techniques rely on inferential methods, i.e. predicting outcomes based on other outcomes and probabilistic reasoning, and draw from a similar assortment of algorithms including principal component analysis, regression analysis, decision trees, and clustering techniques. To add further confusion, the two techniques are commonly mistaken and misreported or even explicitly misused. The textbook *Data mining: Practical machine learning tools and techniques with Java* is said to have originally been titled *Practical machine learning,* but for marketing reasons "data mining" was later appended to the title.[Z]

Lastly, because of their interdisciplinary nature, experts from a diverse spectrum of disciplines often define data mining and machine learning differently. This has led to confusion, in addition to a genuine overlap between the two disciplines. But whereas machine learning emphasizes the incremental process of self-learning and automatically detecting patterns through experience derived from exposure to data, data mining is a less autonomous technique of extracting hidden insight.

Like randomly drilling a hole into the earth's crust, data mining doesn't begin with a clear hypothesis of what insight it will find. Instead, it seeks out patterns and relationships that are yet to be mined and is, thus, well-suited for understanding large datasets with complex patterns. As noted by the authors of *Data Mining: Concepts and Techniques,* data mining developed as a result of advances in data collection and database management beginning in the early 1980s[8] and an urgent need to make sense of progressively larger and complicated datasets.[9]

Whereas data mining focuses on **analyzing input variables to predict a new output**, machine learning extends to **analyzing both input and output variables**. This includes supervised learning techniques that compare known combinations of input and output variables to discern patterns and make predictions, and reinforcement learning which randomly trials a massive number of input variables to produce a desired output. Another machine learning technique, called unsupervised learning, generates predictions based on the analysis of input variables with no known target output. This technique is often used in combination or in preparation for supervised learning under the name of *semi-supervised learning,* and although it overlaps with data mining, unsupervised learning tends to deviate from standard data mining methods such as association and sequence analysis.

Technique	Input is Known	Output is Known	Methodology
Data Mining	✓		Analyzes inputs to generate an unknown output.
Supervised Learning	✓	✓	Analyzes combinations of known inputs and outputs to predict future outputs based on new input data.
Unsupervised Learning	✓		Analyzes inputs to generate an output—algorithms may differ from data mining.
Reinforcement Learning		✓	Randomly trials a high number of input variables to produce a desired output.

Table 1: Comparison of techniques based on the utility of input and output data/variables

To consolidate the difference between data mining and machine learning, let's consider an example of two teams of archaeologists. One team has little knowledge of their target excavation site and imparts domain knowledge to optimize their excavation tools to find patterns and remove debris to reveal hidden artifacts. The team's goal is to manually excavate the area, find new valuable discoveries, and then pack up their equipment and move on. A day later, they fly to another exotic destination to start a new project with no relationship to the site they excavated the day before.

The second team is also in the business of excavating historical sites, but they pursue a different methodology. They refrain from excavating the main pit for several weeks. In this time, they visit other nearby archaeological sites and examine patterns regarding how each archaeological site is constructed. With exposure to each excavation site, they gain experience, thereby improving their ability to interpret patterns and reduce prediction error. When it comes time to excavate the final and most important pit, they execute their understanding and experience of the local terrain to interpret the target site and make predictions.

As is perhaps evident by now, the first team puts their faith in data mining whereas the second team relies on machine learning. While both teams make a living excavating historical sites to discover valuable insight, their goals and methodology are different. The machine learning team invests in self-learning to create a system that uses exposure to data to enhance its capacity to make predictions. The data mining team, meanwhile, concentrates on excavating the target area with a more direct and approximate approach that relies on human intuition rather than self-learning.

We will look more closely at self-learning specific to machine learning in the next chapter and how input and output variables are used to make predictions.

## 3

MACHINE LEARNING CATEGORIES

Machine learning incorporates several hundred statistical-based algorithms and choosing the right algorithm(s) for the job is a constant challenge of working in this field. Before examining specific algorithms, it's important to consolidate one's understanding of the three overarching categories of machine learning and their treatment of input and output variables.

Supervised Learning

Supervised learning imitates our own ability to extract patterns from known examples and use that extracted insight to engineer a repeatable outcome. This is how the car company Toyota designed their first car prototype. Rather than speculate or create a unique process for manufacturing cars, Toyota created its first vehicle prototype after taking apart a Chevrolet car in the corner of their family-run loom business. By observing the finished car (output) and then pulling apart its individual components (input), Toyota's engineers unlocked the design process kept secret by Chevrolet in America.

This process of understanding a known input-output combination is replicated in machine learning using supervised learning. The model analyzes and deciphers the relationship between input and output data to learn the underlying patterns. Input data is referred to as the independent variable (uppercase "X"), while the output data is called the dependent variable (lowercase "y"). An example of a dependent variable (y) might be the coordinates for a rectangle around a person in a digital photo (face recognition), the price of a house, or the class of an item (i.e. sports car, family car, sedan). Their independent variables —which supposedly impact the dependent variable—could be the pixel colors, the size and location of the house, and the specifications of the car respectively. After analyzing a sufficient number of examples, the machine creates a model: an algorithmic equation for producing an output based on patterns from previous input-output examples.

Using the model, the machine can then predict an output based exclusively on the input data. The market price of your used Lexus, for example, can be estimated using the labeled examples of other cars recently sold on a used car website.

	Input	Input	Input	Output
	Card Brand	Mileage (km)	Year of Make	Price (USD)
Car 1	Lexus	51715	2012	15985
Car 2	Lexus	7980	2013	19600
Car 3	Lexus	82497	2012	14095
Car 4	Lexus	85199	2011	12490
Car 5	Audi	62948	2008	13985

Table 2: Extract of a used car dataset

With access to the selling price of other similar cars, the supervised learning model can work backward to determine the relationship between a car's value (output) and its characteristics (input). The input features of your own car can then be inputted into the model to generate a price prediction.

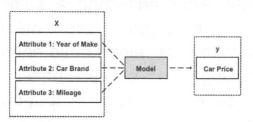

Figure 5: Inputs (X) are fed to the model to generate a new prediction (y)

While input data with an unknown output can be fed to the model to push out a prediction, unlabeled data cannot be used to build the model. When building a supervised learning model, each item (i.e. car, product, customer) must have labeled input and output values—known in data science as a "labeled dataset."

Examples of common algorithms used in supervised learning include regression analysis (i.e. linear regression, logistic regression, non-linear regression), decision trees, *k*-nearest neighbors, neural networks, and support vector machines, each of which are examined in later chapters.

Unsupervised Learning

In the case of unsupervised learning, the output variables are unlabeled, and combinations of input and output variables aren't known. Unsupervised learning instead focuses on analyzing relationships between input variables and uncovering hidden patterns that can be extracted to create new labels regarding possible outputs.

If you group data points based on the purchasing behavior of SME (Small and Medium-sized Enterprises) and large enterprise customers, for example, you're likely to see two clusters of data points emerge. This is because SMEs and large enterprises tend to have different procurement needs. When it comes to purchasing cloud computing infrastructure, for example, essential cloud hosting products and a Content Delivery Network (CDN) should prove sufficient for most SME customers. Large enterprise customers, though, are likely to purchase a broader array of cloud products and complete solutions that include advanced security and networking products like WAF (Web Application Firewall), a dedicated private connection, and VPC (Virtual Private Cloud). By analyzing customer purchasing habits, unsupervised learning is capable of identifying these two groups of customers without specific labels that classify a given company as small/medium or large.

The advantage of unsupervised learning is that it enables you to discover patterns in the data that you were unaware of—such as the presence of two dominant customer types—and provides a springboard for conducting further analysis once new groups are identified. Unsupervised learning is especially compelling in the domain of fraud detection—where the most dangerous attacks are those yet to be classified. One interesting example is DataVisor; a company that has built its business model on unsupervised learning. Founded in 2013 in California, DataVisor protects customers from fraudulent online activities, including spam, fake reviews, fake app installs, and fraudulent transactions. Whereas traditional fraud protection services draw on supervised learning models and rule engines, DataVisor uses unsupervised learning to detect unclassified categories of attacks.

As DataVisor explains on their website, "to detect attacks, existing solutions rely on human experience to create rules or labeled training data to tune models. This means they are unable to detect new attacks that haven't already been identified by humans or labeled in training data." [10] Put another way, traditional solutions analyze chains of activity for a specific type of attack and then create rules to predict and detect repeat attacks. In this case, the dependent variable (output) is the event of an attack, and the independent variables (input) are the common predictor variables of an attack. Examples of independent variables could be:

a) A sudden large order from an unknown user. I.E., established customers might generally spend less than $100 per order, but a new user spends $8,000 on one order immediately upon registering an account.

b) A sudden surge of user ratings. I.E., As with most technology books sold on Amazon.com, the first edition of this book rarely receives more than one reader review per day. In general, approximately 1 in 200 Amazon readers leave a review and most books go weeks or months without a review. However, I notice other authors in this category (data science) attract 50-100 reviews in a single day! (Unsurprisingly, I also see Amazon remove these suspicious reviews weeks or months later.)

c) Identical or similar user reviews from different users. Following the same Amazon analogy, I sometimes see positive reader reviews of my book appear with other books (even with reference to my name as the author still included in the review!). Again, Amazon eventually removes these fake reviews and suspends these accounts for breaking their terms of service.

d) Suspicious shipping address. I.E., For small businesses that routinely ship products to local customers, an order from a distant location (where their products aren't advertised) can, in rare cases, be an indicator of fraudulent or malicious activity.

Standalone activities such as a sudden large order or a remote shipping address might not provide sufficient information to detect sophisticated cybercrime and are probably more likely to lead to a series of false-positive results. But a model that monitors combinations of independent variables, such as a large purchasing order from the other side of the globe or a landslide number of book reviews that reuse existing user content generally leads to a better prediction.

In supervised learning, the model deconstructs and classifies what these common variables are and design a detection system to identify and prevent repeat offenses. Sophisticated cybercriminals, though, learn to evade these simple classification-based rule engines by modifying their tactics. Leading up to an attack, for example, the attackers often register and operate single or multiple accounts and incubate these accounts with activities that mimic legitimate users. They then utilize their established account history to evade detection systems, which closely monitor new users. As a result, solutions that use supervised learning often fail to detect sleeper cells until the damage has been inflicted and especially for new types of attacks.

DataVisor and other anti-fraud solution providers instead leverage unsupervised learning techniques to address these limitations. They analyze patterns across hundreds of millions of accounts and identify suspicious connections between users (input)—without knowing the actual category of future attacks (output). By grouping and identifying malicious actors whose actions deviate from standard user behavior, companies can take actions to prevent new types of attacks (whose outcomes are still unknown and unlabeled).

Examples of suspicious actions may include the four cases listed earlier or new instances of unnormal behavior such as a pool of newly registered users with the same profile picture. By identifying these subtle correlations across users, fraud detection companies like DataVisor can locate sleeper cells in their incubation stage. A swarm of fake Facebook accounts, for example, might be linked as friends and like the same pages but aren't linked with genuine users. As this type of fraudulent behavior relies on fabricated interconnections between accounts, unsupervised learning thereby helps to uncover collaborators and expose criminal rings.

The drawback, though, of using unsupervised learning is that because the dataset is unlabeled, there aren't any known output observations to check and validate the model, and predictions are therefore more subjective than those coming from supervised learning.

We will cover unsupervised learning later in this book specific to *k*-means clustering. Other examples of unsupervised learning algorithms include social network analysis and descending dimension algorithms.

Semi-supervised Learning

A hybrid form of unsupervised and supervised learning is also available in the form of semi-supervised learning, which is used for datasets that contain a mix of labeled and unlabeled cases. With the "more data the better" as a core motivator, the goal of semi-supervised learning is to leverage unlabeled cases to improve the reliability of the prediction model. One technique is to build the initial model using the labeled cases (supervised learning) and then use the same model to label the remaining cases (that are unlabeled) in the dataset. The model can then be retrained using a larger dataset (with less or no unlabeled cases). Alternatively, the model could be iteratively re-trained using newly labeled cases that meet a set threshold of confidence and adding the new cases to the training data after they meet the set threshold. There is, however, no guarantee that a semi-supervised model will outperform a model trained with less data (based exclusively on the original labeled cases).

Reinforcement Learning

Reinforcement learning is the third and most advanced category of machine learning. Unlike supervised and unsupervised learning, reinforcement learning builds its prediction model by gaining feedback from random trial and error and leveraging insight from previous iterations.

The goal of reinforcement learning is to achieve a specific goal (output) by randomly trialing a vast number of possible input combinations and grading their performance.

Reinforcement learning can be complicated to understand and is probably best explained using a video game analogy. As a player progresses through the virtual space of a game, they learn the value of various actions under different conditions and grow more familiar with the field of play. Those learned values then inform and influence the player's subsequent behavior and their performance gradually improves based on learning and experience.

Reinforcement learning is similar, where algorithms are set to train the model based on continuous learning. A standard reinforcement learning model has measurable performance criteria where outputs are graded. In the case of self-driving vehicles, avoiding a crash earns a positive score, and in the case of chess, avoiding defeat likewise receives a positive assessment.

Q-learning

A specific algorithmic example of reinforcement learning is Q-learning. In Q-learning, you start with a set environment of *states,* represented as "S." In the game Pac-Man, states could be the challenges, obstacles or pathways that exist in the video game. There may exist a wall to the left, a ghost to the right, and a power pill above—each representing different states. The set of possible actions to respond to these states is referred to as "A." In Pac-Man, actions are limited to left, right, up, and down movements, as well as multiple combinations thereof. The third important symbol is "Q," which is the model's starting value and has an initial value of "0."

As Pac-Man explores the space inside the game, two main things happen:

1) Q drops as negative things occur after a given state/action.

2) Q increases as positive things occur after a given state/action.

In Q-learning, the machine learns to match the action for a given state that generates or preserves the highest level of Q. It learns initially through the process of random movements (actions) under different conditions (states). The model records its results (rewards and penalties) and how they impact its Q level and stores those values to inform and optimize its future actions.

While this sounds simple, implementation is computationally expensive and beyond the scope of an absolute beginner's introduction to machine learning. Reinforcement learning algorithms aren't covered in this book, but, I'll leave you with a link to a more comprehensive explanation of reinforcement learning and

Q-learning using the Pac-Man case study.

https://inst.eecs.berkeley.edu/~cs188/sp12/projects/rein
forcement/reinforcement.html

## 4

THE MACHINE LEARNING TOOLBOX

A handy way to learn a new skill is to visualize a toolbox of the essential tools and materials of that subject area. For instance, given the task of packing a dedicated toolbox to build a website, you would first need to add a selection of programming languages. This would include frontend languages such as HTML, CSS, and JavaScript, one or two backend programming languages based on personal preferences, and of course, a text editor. You might throw in a website builder such as WordPress and then pack another compartment with web hosting, DNS, and maybe a few domain names that you've purchased.

This is not an extensive inventory, but from this general list, you start to gain a better appreciation of what tools you need to master on the path to becoming a successful web developer.

Let's now unpack the basic toolbox for machine learning.

Compartment 1: Data

Stored in the first compartment of the toolbox is your data. Data constitutes the input needed to train your model and generate predictions. Data comes in many forms, including structured and unstructured data. As a beginner, it's best to start with (analyzing) structured data. This means that the data is defined, organized, and labeled in a table, as shown in Table 3. Images, videos, email messages, and audio recordings are examples of unstructured data as they don't fit into the organized structure of rows and columns.

Date	Bitcoin Price	No. of Days Transpired
19-05-2015	234.31	1
14-01-2016	431.76	240
09-07-2016	652.14	417
15-01-2017	817.26	607
24-05-2017	2358.96	736

Table 3: Bitcoin Prices from 2015-2017

Before we proceed, I first want to explain the anatomy of a tabular dataset. A tabular (table-based) dataset contains data organized in rows and columns. Contained in each column is a *feature*. A feature is also known as a *variable,* a *dimension* or an *attribute*—but they all mean the same thing. Each row represents a single observation of a given feature/variable. Rows are sometimes referred to as a *case* or *value*, but in this book, we use the term "row."

	Vector	Matrices	
	Feature 1	Feature 2	Feature 3
Row 1			
Row 2			
Row 3			
Row 4			

Figure 6: Example of a tabular dataset

Each column is known also as a *vector.* Vectors store your X and y values and multiple vectors (columns) are commonly referred to as *matrices.* In the case of supervised learning, y will already exist in your dataset and be used to identify patterns in relation to the independent variables (X). The y values are commonly expressed in the final vector, as shown in Figure 7.

	Vector	Matrices		
	Maker (X)	Year (X)	Model (X)	Price (y)
Row 1				
Row 2				
Row 3				
Row 4				

Figure 7: The y value is often but not always expressed in the far-right vector

Scatterplots, including 2-D, 3-D, and 4-D plots, are also packed into the first compartment of the toolbox with the data. A 2-D scatterplot consists of a vertical axis (known as the y-axis) and a horizontal axis (known as the x-axis) and provides the graphical canvas to plot variable combinations, known as data points. Each data point on the scatterplot represents an observation from the dataset with X values on the x-axis and y values on the y-axis.

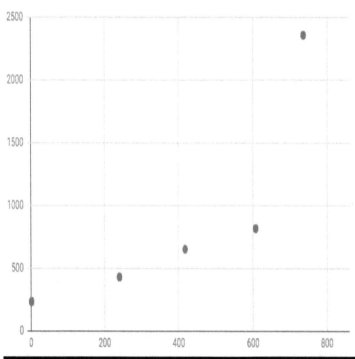

	Independent Variable (X)	Dependent Variable (y)
Row 1	1	243.31
Row 2	240	431.76
Row 3	417	653.14
Row 4	607	817.26
Row 5	736	2358.96

Figure 8: Example of a 2-D scatterplot. X represents days passed and y is Bitcoin price.

Compartment 2: Infrastructure

The second compartment of the toolbox contains your machine learning infrastructure, which consists of platforms and tools for processing data. As a beginner to machine learning, you are likely to be using a web application (such as Jupyter Notebook) and a programming language like Python. There are then a series of machine learning libraries, including NumPy, Pandas, and Scikit-learn, which are compatible with Python. Machine learning libraries are a collection of pre-compiled programming routines frequently used in machine learning that enable you to manipulate data and execute algorithms with minimal use of code.

You will also need a machine to process your data, in the form of a physical computer or a virtual server. In addition, you may need specialized libraries for data visualization such as Seaborn and Matplotlib, or a standalone software program like Tableau, which supports a range of visualization techniques including charts, graphs, maps, and other visual options.

With your infrastructure sprayed across the table (hypothetically of course), you're now ready to build your first machine learning model. The first step is to crank up your computer. Standard desktop computers and laptops are both sufficient for working with smaller datasets that are stored in a central location, such as a CSV file. You then need to install a programming environment, such as Jupyter Notebook, and a programming language, which for most beginners is Python.

Python is the most widely used programming language for machine learning because:

a) It's easy to learn and operate.

b) It's compatible with a range of machine learning libraries.

c) It can be used for related tasks, including data collection (web scraping) and data piping (Hadoop and Spark).

Other go-to languages for machine learning include C and C++. If you're proficient with C and C++, then it makes sense to stick with what you know. C and C++ are the default programming languages for advanced machine learning because they can run directly on the GPU (Graphical Processing Unit). Python needs to be converted before it can run on the GPU, but we'll get to this and what a GPU is later in the chapter.

Next, Python users will need to import the following libraries: NumPy, Pandas, and Scikit-learn. NumPy is a free and open-source library that allows you to efficiently load and work with large datasets, including merging datasets and managing matrices.

Scikit-learn provides access to a range of popular shallow algorithms, including linear regression, clustering techniques, decision trees, and support vector machines. Shallow learning algorithms refer to learning algorithms that predict outcomes directly from the input features. Non-shallow algorithms or deep learning, meanwhile, produce an output based on preceding layers in the model (discussed in Chapter 13 in reference to artificial neural networks) rather than directly from the input features.[11]

Finally, Pandas enables your data to be represented as a virtual spreadsheet that you can control and manipulate using code. It shares many of the same features as Microsoft Excel in that it allows you to edit data and perform calculations. The name Pandas derives from the term "panel data," which refers to its ability to create a series of panels, similar to "sheets" in Excel. Pandas is also ideal for importing and extracting data from CSV files.

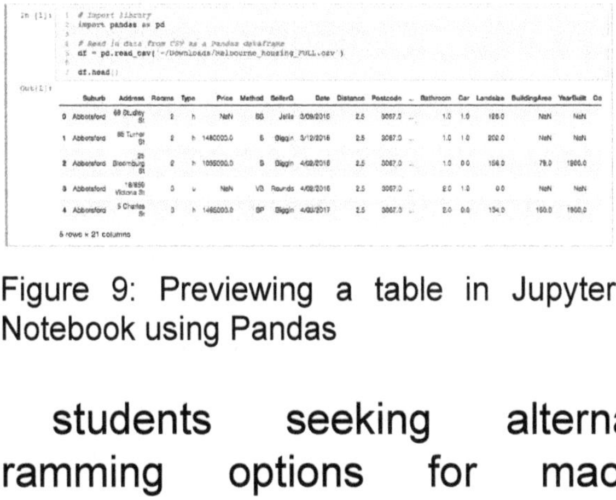

Figure 9: Previewing a table in Jupyter Notebook using Pandas

For students seeking alternative programming options for machine learning beyond Python, C, and C++, there is also R, MATLAB, and Octave.

R is a free and open-source programming language optimized for mathematical operations and useful for building matrices and performing statistical functions. Although more commonly used for data mining, R also supports machine learning.

The two direct competitors to R are MATLAB and Octave. MATLAB is a commercial and proprietary programming language that is strong at solving algebraic equations and is a quick programming language to learn. MATLAB is widely used in the fields of electrical engineering, chemical engineering, civil engineering, and aeronautical engineering. Computer scientists and computer engineers, however, tend not to use MATLAB and especially in recent years. MATLAB, though, is still widely used in academia for machine learning. Thus, while you may see MATLAB featured in online courses for machine learning, and especially Coursera, this is not to say that it's as commonly used in industry. If, however, you're coming from an engineering background, MATLAB is certainly a logical choice.

Lastly, there is Octave, which is essentially a free version of MATLAB developed in response to MATLAB by the open-source community.

Compartment 3: Algorithms

Now that the development environment is set up and you've chosen your programming language and libraries, you can next import your data directly from a CSV file. You can find hundreds of interesting datasets in CSV format from kaggle.com. After registering as a Kaggle member, you can download a dataset of your choosing. Best of all, Kaggle datasets are free, and there's no cost to register as a user. The dataset will download directly to your computer as a CSV file, which means you can use Microsoft Excel to open and even perform basic algorithms such as linear regression on your dataset.

Next is the third and final compartment that stores the machine learning algorithms. Beginners typically start out using simple supervised learning algorithms such as linear regression, logistic regression, decision trees, and *k*-nearest neighbors. Beginners are also likely to apply unsupervised learning in the form of *k*-means clustering and descending dimension algorithms.

Visualization

No matter how impactful and insightful your data discoveries are, you need a way to communicate the results to relevant decision-makers. This is where data visualization comes in handy to highlight and communicate findings from the data to a general audience. The visual story conveyed through graphs, scatterplots, heatmaps, box plots, and the representation of numbers as shapes make for quick and easy storytelling.

In general, the less informed your audience is, the more important it is to visualize your findings. Conversely, if your audience is knowledgeable about the topic, additional details and technical terms can be used to supplement visual elements. To visualize your results, you can draw on a software program like Tableau or a Python library such as Seaborn, which are stored in the second compartment of the toolbox.

The Advanced Toolbox

We have so far examined the starter toolbox for a beginner, but what about an advanced user? What does their toolbox look like? While it may take some time before you get to work with more advanced tools, it doesn't hurt to take a sneak peek.

The advanced toolbox comes with a broader spectrum of tools and, of course, data. One of the biggest differences between a beginner and an expert is the kind of data they manage and operate. Beginners work with small datasets that are easy to handle and downloaded directly to one's desktop as a simple CSV file. Advanced users, though, will be eager to tackle massive datasets, well in the vicinity of big data. This might mean that the data is stored across multiple locations, and its composition is streamed (imported and analyzed in real-time) rather than static, which makes the data itself a moving target.

Compartment 1: Big Data

Big data is used to describe a dataset that, due to its variety, volume, and velocity, defies conventional methods of processing and would be impossible for a human to process without the assistance of advanced technology. Big data doesn't have an exact definition in terms of size or a minimum threshold of rows and columns. At the moment, petabytes qualify as big data, but datasets are becoming increasingly bigger as we find new ways to collect and store data at a lower cost.

Big data is also less likely to fit into standard rows and columns and may contain numerous data types, such as structured data and a range of unstructured data, i.e. images, videos, email messages, and audio files.

Compartment 2: Infrastructure

Given that advanced learners are dealing with up to petabytes of data, robust infrastructure is required. Instead of relying on the CPU of a personal computer, the experts typically turn to distributed computing and a cloud provider such as Amazon Web Services

(AWS) or Google Cloud Platform to run their data processing on a virtual graphics processing unit (GPU). As a specialized parallel computing chip, GPU instances are able to perform many more floating-point operations per second than a CPU, allowing for much faster solutions with linear algebra and statistics than with a CPU.

GPU chips were originally added to PC motherboards and video consoles such as the PlayStation 2 and the Xbox for gaming purposes. They were developed to accelerate the rendering of images with millions of pixels whose frames needed to be continuously recalculated to display output in less than a second. By 2005, GPU chips were produced in such large quantities that prices dropped dramatically and they became almost a commodity. Although popular in the video game industry, their application in the space of machine learning wasn't fully understood or realized until quite recently. Kevin Kelly, in his novel *The Inevitable: Understanding the 12 Technological Forces That Will Shape Our Future*, explains that in 2009, Andrew Ng and a team at Stanford University made a discovery to link inexpensive GPU clusters to run neural networks consisting of hundreds of millions of connected nodes.

"Traditional processors required several weeks to calculate all the cascading possibilities in a neural net with one hundred million parameters. Ng found that a cluster of GPUs could accomplish the same thing in a day," explains Kelly. [12]

As mentioned, C and C++ are the preferred languages to directly edit and perform mathematical operations on the GPU. Python can also be used and converted into C in combination with a machine learning library such as TensorFlow from Google. Although it's possible to run TensorFlow on a CPU, you can gain up to about 1,000x in performance using the GPU. Unfortunately for Mac users, TensorFlow is only compatible with the Nvidia GPU card, which is no longer available with Mac OS X. Mac users can still run

TensorFlow on their CPU but will need to run their workload on the cloud if they wish to use a GPU.

Amazon Web Services, Microsoft Azure, Alibaba Cloud, Google Cloud Platform, and other cloud providers offer pay-as-you-go GPU resources, which may also start off free using a free trial program. Google Cloud Platform is currently regarded as a leading choice for virtual GPU resources based on performance and pricing. Google also announced in 2016 that it would publicly release a Tensor Processing Unit designed specifically for running TensorFlow, which is already used internally at Google.

Compartment 3: Advanced Algorithms

To round out this chapter, let's take a look at the third compartment of the advanced toolbox containing machine learning algorithms. To analyze large datasets and respond to complicated prediction tasks, advanced practitioners work with a plethora of algorithms including Markov models, support vector machines, and Q-learning, as well as combinations of algorithms to create a unified model, known as ensemble modeling (explored further in Chapter 15). However, the algorithm family they're most likely to work with is artificial neural networks (introduced in Chapter 13), which comes with its own selection of advanced machine learning libraries.

While Scikit-learn offers a range of popular shallow algorithms, TensorFlow is the machine learning library of choice for deep learning/neural networks. It supports numerous advanced techniques including automatic calculus for back-propagation/gradient descent. The depth of resources, documentation, and jobs available with TensorFlow also make it an obvious framework to learn. Popular alternative libraries for neural networks include Torch, Caffe, and the fast-growing Keras.

Written in Python, Keras is an open-source deep learning library that runs on top of TensorFlow, Theano, and other frameworks, which allows users to perform fast experimentation in fewer lines of code. Similar to a WordPress website theme, Keras is minimal, modular, and quick to get up and running. It is, however, less flexible in comparison to TensorFlow and other libraries. Developers, therefore, will sometimes utilize Keras to validate their decision model before switching to TensorFlow to build a more customized model.

Caffe is also open-source and is typically used to develop deep learning architectures for image classification and image segmentation. Caffe is written in C++ but has a Python interface that supports GPU-based acceleration using the Nvidia cuDNN chip.

Released in 2002, Torch is also well established in the deep learning community and is used at Facebook, Google, Twitter, NYU, IDIAP, Purdue University as well as other companies and research labs.[13] Based on the programming language Lua, Torch is open-source and offers a range of algorithms and functions used for deep learning.

Theano was another competitor to TensorFlow until recently, but as of late

2017, contributions to the framework have officially ceased.[14]

## 5

DATA SCRUBBING

Like most varieties of fruit, datasets need upfront cleaning and human manipulation before they're ready for consumption. The "clean-up" process applies to machine learning and many other fields of data science and is known in the industry as *data scrubbing*. This is the technical process of refining your dataset to make it more workable. This might involve modifying and removing incomplete, incorrectly formatted, irrelevant or duplicated data. It might also entail converting text-based data to numeric values and the redesigning of features.

For data practitioners, data scrubbing typically demands the greatest application of time and effort.

Feature Selection

To generate the best results from your data, it's essential to identify which variables are most relevant to your hypothesis or objective. In practice, this means being selective in choosing the variables you include in your model. Moreover, preserving features that don't correlate strongly with the output value can manipulate and derail the model's accuracy. Let's consider the following data excerpt downloaded from kaggle.com documenting dying languages.

Name in English	Name in Spanish	Countries	Country Code	Num. of Speakers
South Italian	Napolitano-calabres	Italy	ITA	7500000
Sicilian	Siciliano	Italy	ITA	5000000
Low Saxon	Bajo Sajón	Germany, Denmark, Netherlands, Poland, Russian Federation	DEU, DNK, NLD, POL, RUS	4800000
Belarusian	Bielorruso	Belarus, Latvia, Lithuania, Poland, Russian Federation, Ukraine	BRB, LVA, LTU, POL, RUS, UKR	4000000
Lombard	Lombardo	Italy, Switzerland	ITA, CHE	3500000
Romani	Romaní	Albania, Germany, Austria, Belarus, Bosnia and Herzegovina, Bulgaria, Croatia, Estonia, Finland, France, Greece, Hungary, Italy, Latvia, Lithuania, The former Yugoslav Republic of Macedonia, Netherlands, Poland, Romania, United Kingdom of Great Britain and Northern Ireland, Russian Federation, Slovakia, Slovenia, Switzerland, Czech Republic, Turkey, Ukraine, Serbia, Montenegro	ALB, DEU, AUT, BRB, BIH, BGR, HRV, EST, FIN, FRA, GRC, HUN, ITA, LVA, LTU, MKD, NLD, POL, ROU, GBR, RUS, SVK, SVN, CHE, CZE, TUR, UKR, SRB, MNE	3500000
Yiddish	Yiddish	Israel	ISR	3000000
Gondi	Gondi	India	IND	2713790

Table 4: Endangered languages, database: https://www.kaggle.com/the-guardian/extinct-languages

Let's say our goal is to identify variables that contribute to a language becoming endangered. Based on the purpose of our analysis, it's unlikely that a language's "Name in Spanish" will lead to any relevant insight. We can therefore delete this vector (column) from the dataset. This helps to prevent over-complication and potential inaccuracies as well as improve the overall processing speed of the model.

Secondly, the dataset contains duplicated information in the form of separate vectors for "Countries" and "Country Code." Analyzing both of these vectors doesn't provide any additional insight; hence, we can choose to delete one and retain the other.

Another method to reduce the number of features is to roll multiple features into one, as shown in the following example.

	Protein Shake	Nike Sneakers	Adidas Boots	Fitbit	Powerade	Protein Bar	Fitness Watch	Vitamins
Buyer 1	1	1	0	1	0	5	1	0
Buyer 2	0	0	0	0	0	0	0	1
Buyer 3	3	0	1	0	5	0	0	0
Buyer 4	1	1	0	0	10	1	0	0

Table 5: Sample product inventory

Contained in Table 5 is a list of products sold on an e-commerce platform. The dataset comprises four buyers and eight products. This is not a large sample size of buyers and products—due in part to the spatial limitations of the book format. A real-life e-commerce platform would have many more columns to work with but let's go ahead with this simplified example.

To analyze the data more efficiently, we can reduce the number of columns by merging similar features into fewer columns. For instance, we can remove individual product names and replace the eight product items with fewer categories or subtypes. As all product items fall under the category of "fitness," we can sort by product subtype and compress the columns from eight to three. The three newly created product subtype columns are "Health Food," "Apparel," and "Digital."

	Health Food	Apparel	Digital
Buyer 1	6	1	2
Buyer 2	1	0	0
Buyer 3	8	1	0
Buyer 4	12	1	0

Table 6: Synthesized product inventory

This enables us to transform the dataset in a way that preserves and captures information using fewer variables. The downside to this transformation is that we have less information about the relationships between specific products. Rather than recommending products to users according to other individual products, recommendations will instead be based on associations between product subtypes or recommendations of the same product subtype.

Nonetheless, this approach still upholds a high level of data relevancy. Buyers will be recommended health food when they buy other health food or when they buy apparel (depending on the degree of correlation), and obviously not machine learning textbooks—unless it turns out that there is a strong correlation there!

But alas, such a variable/category is outside the frame of this dataset.

Remember that data reduction is also a business decision and business owners in counsel with their data science team must consider the trade-off between convenience and the overall precision of the model.

Row Compression

In addition to feature selection, you may need to reduce the number of rows and thereby compress the total number of data points. This may involve merging two or more rows into one, as shown in the following dataset, with "Tiger" and "Lion" merged and renamed as "Carnivore."

Before

Animal	Meat Eater	Legs	Tail	Race Time
Tiger	Yes	4	Yes	2:01 mins
Lion	Yes	4	Yes	2:05 mins
Tortoise	No	4	No	55:02 mins

After

Animal	Meat Eater	Legs	Tail	Race Time
Carnivore	Yes	4	Yes	2:03 mins
Tortoise	No	4	No	55:02 mins

Table 7: Example of row merge

By merging these two rows (Tiger & Lion), the feature values for both rows must also be aggregated and recorded in a single row. In this case, it's possible to merge the two rows because they possess the same categorical values for all features except Race Time—which can be easily aggregated. The race time of the Tiger and the Lion can be added and divided by two.

Numeric values are normally easy to aggregate given they are not categorical. For instance, it would be impossible to aggregate an animal with four legs and an animal with two legs! We obviously can't merge these two animals and set "three" as the aggregate number of legs.

Row compression can also be challenging to implement in cases where numeric values aren't available. For example, the values "Japan" and "Argentina" are very difficult to merge. The values "Japan" and "South Korea" can be merged, as they can be categorized as countries from the same continent, "Asia" or "East Asia." However, if we add "Pakistan" and "Indonesia" to the same group, we may begin to see skewed results, as there are significant cultural, religious, economic, and other dissimilarities between these four countries.

In summary, non-numeric and categorical row values can be problematic to merge while preserving the true value of the original data. Also, row compression is usually less attainable than feature compression and especially for datasets with a high number of features.

One-hot Encoding

After finalizing the features and rows to be included in your model, you next want to look for text-based values that can be converted into numbers. Aside from set text-based values such as True/False (that automatically convert to "1" and "0" respectively), most algorithms are not compatible with non-numeric data.

One method to convert text-based values into numeric values is *one-hot encoding*, which transforms values into binary form, represented as "1" or "0"—"True" or

"False." A "0," representing False, means that the value does not belong to a given feature, whereas a "1"—True or "hot"— confirms that the value does belong to that feature.

Below is another excerpt from the dying languages dataset which we can use to observe one-hot encoding.

Name in English	Speakers	Degree of Endangerment
South Italian	7500000	Vulnerable
Sicilian	5000000	Vulnerable
Low Saxon	4800000	Vulnerable
Belarusian	4000000	Vulnerable
Lombard	3500000	Definitely endangered
Romani	3500000	Definitely endangered
Yiddish	3000000	Definitely endangered
Gondi	2713790	Vulnerable
Picard	700000	Severely endangered

Table 8: Endangered languages

Before we begin, note that the values contained in the "No. of Speakers" column do not contain commas or spaces, e.g., 7,500,000 and 7 500 000. Although formatting makes large numbers easier for human interpretation, programming languages don't require such niceties. Formatting numbers can lead to an invalid syntax or trigger an unwanted result, depending on the programming language—so remember to keep numbers unformatted for programming purposes. Feel free, though, to add spacing or commas at the data visualization stage, as this will make it easier for your audience to interpret and especially when presenting large numbers.

On the right-hand side of the table is a vector categorizing the degree of endangerment of nine different languages. We can convert this column into numeric values by applying the one-hot encoding method, as demonstrated in the subsequent table.

Name in English	Speakers	Vulnerable	Definitely Endangered	Severely Endangered
South Italian	7500000	1	0	0
Sicilian	5000000	1	0	0
Low Saxon	4800000	1	0	0
Belarusian	4000000	1	0	0
Lombard	3500000	0	1	0
Romani	3500000	0	1	0
Yiddish	3000000	0	1	0
Gondi	2713790	1	0	0
Picard	700000	0	0	1

Table 9: Example of one-hot encoding

Using one-hot encoding, the dataset has expanded to five columns, and we have created three new features from the original feature (Degree of Endangerment). We have also set each column value to "1" or "0," depending on the value of the original feature. This now makes it possible for us to input the data into our model and choose from a broader spectrum of machine learning algorithms. The downside is that we have more dataset features, which may slightly extend processing time. This is usually manageable but *can* be problematic for datasets where the original features are split into a large number of new features.

One hack to minimize the total number of features is to restrict binary cases to a single column. As an example, a speed dating dataset on kaggle.com lists "Gender" in a single column using one-hot encoding. Rather than create discrete columns for both "Male" and "Female," they merged these two features into one. According to the dataset's key, females are denoted as "0" and males as "1." The creator of the dataset also used this technique for "Same Race" and "Match."

Subject Number ID	Gender	Same Race	Age	Match
1	0	0	27	0
1	0	0	22	0
1	0	1	22	1
1	0	0	23	1
1	0	0	24	1
1	0	0	25	0
1	0	0	30	0

Gender:	Same Race:	Match:
Female = 0	No = 0	No = 0
Male = 1	Yes = 1	Yes = 1

Table 10: Speed dating results, database: https://www.kaggle.com/annavictoria/speed-dating-experiment

Binning

Binning (also called bucketing) is another method of feature engineering but is used for converting continuous numeric values into multiple binary features called bins or buckets according to their range of values.

Whoa, hold on! Aren't numeric values a good thing? Yes, in most cases continuous numeric values are preferred as they are compatible with a broader selection of algorithms. Where numeric values are not ideal, is in situations where they list variations irrelevant to the goals of your analysis.

Let's take house price evaluation as an example. The exact measurements of a tennis court might not matter much when evaluating house property prices; the relevant information is whether the property *has* a tennis court. This logic probably also applies to the garage and the swimming pool, where the existence or non-existence of the variable is generally more influential than their specific measurements.

The solution here is to replace the numeric measurements of the tennis court with a True/False feature or a categorical value such as "small," "medium," and "large." Another alternative would be to apply one-hot encoding with "0" for homes that *do not* have a tennis court and "1" for homes that *do* have a tennis court.

Normalization

While machine learning algorithms can run without using the next two techniques, normalization and standardization help to improve model accuracy when used with the right algorithm. The former (normalization) rescales the range of values for a given feature into a set range with a prescribed minimum and maximum, such as [0, 1] or [−1, 1]. By containing the range of the feature, this technique helps to normalize the variance among the dataset's features which may otherwise be exaggerated by another factor. The variance of a feature measured in centimeters, for example, might distract the algorithm from another feature with a similar or higher degree of variance but that is measured in meters or another metric that downplays the actual variance of the feature.

Normalization, however, usually isn't recommended for rescaling features with an extreme range as the normalized range is too narrow to emphasize extremely high or low feature values.

Standardization

A better technique for emphasizing high or low feature values is standardization. This technique converts unit variance to a standard normal distribution with a mean of zero and a standard deviation (σ) of one.[15] This means that an extremely high or low value would be expressed as three or more standard deviations from the mean.

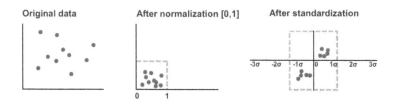

Original data   After normalization [0,1]   After standardization

Figure 10: Examples of rescaled data using normalization and standardization

Standardization is generally more effective than normalization when the variability of the feature reflects a bell-curve shape of normal distribution and is often used in unsupervised learning. In other situations, normalization and standardization can be applied separately and compared for accuracy.

Standardization generally recommended when preparing data for support vector machines (SVM), principal component analysis (PCA), and *k*-nearest neighbors (*k*-NN).

Missing Data

Dealing with missing data is never a desired situation. Imagine unpacking a jigsaw puzzle with five percent of the pieces missing. Missing values in your dataset can be equally frustrating and interfere with your analysis and the model's predictions. There are, however, strategies to minimize the negative impact of missing data.

One approach is to approximate missing values using the *mode* value. The mode represents the single most common variable value available in the dataset. This works best with categorical and binary variable types, such as one to five-star rating systems and positive/negative drug tests respectively.

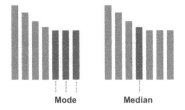

Figure 11: A visual example of the mode and median respectively

The second approach is to approximate missing values using the *median* value, which adopts the value(s) located in the middle of the dataset. This works best with continuous variables, which have an infinite number of possible values, such as house prices.

As a last resort, rows with missing values can be removed altogether. The obvious downside to this approach is having less data to analyze and potentially less comprehensive insight.

## 6

SETTING UP YOUR DATA

After cleaning your dataset, the next job is to split the data into two segments for training and testing, also known as *split validation*. The ratio of the two splits is usually 70/30 or 80/20. This means, assuming that your variables are expressed horizontally and instances vertically (as shown in Figure 12), that your training data should account for 70 percent to 80 percent of the rows in your dataset, and the remaining 20 percent to 30 percent of rows are left for your test data.

	Variable 1	Variable 2	Variable 3
Row 1			
Row 2			
Row 3			
Row 4			
Row 5			
Row 6			
Row 7			
Row 8			
Row 9			
Row 10			

Figure 12: 70/30 partitioning of training and test data

While it's common to split the data 70/30 or 80/20, there is no set rule for preparing a training-test split. Given the growing size of modern datasets (with upwards of a million or more rows), it might be optimal to use a less even split such as 90/10 as this will give you more data to train your model while having enough data left over to test your model.

Before you split your data, it's essential that you randomize the row order. This helps to avoid bias in your model, as your original dataset might be arranged alphabetically or sequentially according to when the data was collected. If you don't randomize the data, you may accidentally omit significant variance from the training data that can cause unwanted surprises when you apply the training model to your test data. Fortunately, Scikit-learn provides a built-in command to shuffle and randomize your data with just one line of code as demonstrated in Chapter 17.

After randomizing the data, you can begin to design your model and apply it to the training data. The remaining 30 percent or so of data is put to the side and reserved for testing the accuracy of the model later; it's imperative not to test your model with the same data you used for training. In the case of supervised learning, the model is developed by feeding the machine the training data and analyzing relationships between the features (X) of the input data and the final output (y).

The next step is to measure how well the model performed. There is a range of performance metrics and choosing the right method depends on the application of the model. Area under the curve (AUC) – Receiver Operating Characteristic

(ROC)[16], confusion matrix, recall, and accuracy are four examples of performance metrics used with classification tasks such as an email spam detection system. Meanwhile, mean absolute error and root mean square error (RMSE) are commonly used to assess models that provide a numeric output such as a predicted house value.

In this book, we use mean absolute error (MAE), which measures the average of the errors in a set of predictions on a numeric/continuous scale, i.e. how far is the regression hyperplane to a given data point. Using Scikit-learn, mean absolute error is found by inputting the X values from the training data into the model and generating a prediction for each row in the dataset. Scikit-learn compares the predictions of the model to the correct output (y) and measures the model's accuracy. You'll know that the model is accurate when the error rate for the training and test dataset is low, which means the model has learned the dataset's underlying trends and patterns. If the average recorded MAE or RMSE is much higher using the test data than the training data, this is usually an indication of overfitting (discussed in Chapter 11) in the model. Once the model can adequately predict the values of the test data, it's ready to use in the wild.

If the model fails to predict values from the test data accurately, check that the training and test data were randomized. Next, you may need to modify the model's hyperparameters. Each algorithm has hyperparameters; these are your algorithm's learning settings(and not the settings of the actual model itself). In simple terms, hyperparameters control and impact how fast the model learns patterns and which patterns to identify and analyze. Discussion of algorithm hyperparameters and optimization is discussed in Chapter 11 and Chapter 18.

Cross Validation

While split validation can be effective for developing models using existing data, question marks naturally arise over whether the model can remain accurate when used on new data. If your existing dataset is too small to construct a precise model, or if the training/test partition of data is not appropriate, this may later lead to poor predictions with live data.

Fortunately, there is a valid workaround for this problem. Rather than split the data into two segments (one for training and one for testing), you can implement what's called *cross validation*. Cross validation maximizes the availability of training data by splitting data into various combinations and testing each specific combination.

Cross validation can be performed using one of two primary methods. The first method is *exhaustive cross validation*, which involves finding and testing all possible combinations to divide the original sample into a training set and a test set. The alternative and more common method is non-exhaustive cross validation, known as *k-fold validation*. The *k*-fold validation technique involves splitting data into *k* assigned buckets and reserving one of those buckets for testing the training model at each round.

To perform *k*-fold validation, data are randomly assigned to *k* number of equal-sized buckets. One bucket is reserved as the test bucket and is used to measure and evaluate the performance of the remaining (*k*-1) buckets.

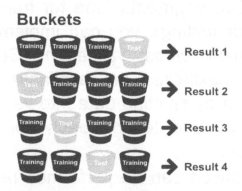

Figure 13: *k*-fold validation

The cross validation technique is repeated *k* number of times ("folds"). At each fold, one bucket is reserved to test the training model generated by the other buckets. The process is repeated until all buckets have been utilized as both a training and test set. The results are then aggregated and combined to formulate a single model.

By using all available data for both training and testing and averaging the model's outputs, the *k*-fold validation technique minimizes the prediction error normally incurred by relying on a fixed training-test split. This method, though, is slower because the training process is multiplied by the number of validation sets.

How Much Data Do I Need?

A common question for students starting out in machine learning *is how much data do I need to train my model?* In general, machine learning works best when your training dataset includes a full range of feature combinations.

What does a full range of feature combinations look like? Imagine you have a dataset about data scientists categorized into the following features:
- University degree (X)
- 5+ years of professional experience (X)
- Children (X)
- Salary (y)

To assess the relationship that the first three features (X) have to a data scientist's salary (y), we need a dataset that includes the y value for each combination of features. For instance, we need to know the salary for data scientists with a university degree and 5+ years of professional experience who <u>don't</u> have children, as well as data scientists with a university degree and 5+ years of professional experience that <u>do</u> have children.

The more available combinations in the dataset, the more effective the model is at capturing how each attribute affects y (the data scientist's salary). This ensures that when it comes to putting the model into practice on the test data or live data, it won't unravel at the sight of unseen combinations.

At an absolute minimum, a basic machine learning model should contain ten times as many data points as the total number of features. So, for a small dataset with 5 features, the training data should ideally have at least 50 rows. Datasets with a large number of features, though, require a higher number of data points as combinations grow exponentially with more variables.

Generally, the more relevant data you have available as training data, the more combinations you can incorporate into your prediction model, which can help to produce more accurate predictions. In some cases, it might not be possible or cost-effective to source data covering all possible combinations, and you may have to make do with what you have at your disposal. Conversely, there is a natural diminishing rate of return after an adequate volume of training data (that's widely representative of the problem) has been reached.

The last important consideration is matching your data to an algorithm. For datasets with less than 10,000 samples, clustering and dimensionality reduction algorithms can be highly effective, whereas regression analysis and classification algorithms are more suitable for datasets with less than 100,000 samples. Neural networks require even more samples to run effectively and are more cost-effective and time-efficient for working with massive quantities of data.

For more information, Scikit-learn has a cheat-sheet for matching algorithms to different datasets at http://scikit-learn.org/stable/tutorial/machine_learning _map/.

The following chapters examine specific algorithms commonly used in machine learning. Please note that I include some equations out of necessity, and I have tried to keep them as simple as possible. Many of the machine learning techniques that are discussed in this book already have working implementations in your programming language of choice with no equation solving required.

You can also find video tutorials on how to code models in Python using algorithms mentioned in this book. You can find these free video tutorials at https://scatterplotpress.com/p/ml-code-exercises.

## 7

LINEAR REGRESSION

As the "Hello World" of supervised learning algorithms, regression analysis is a simple technique for predicting an unknown variable using the results you do know. The first regression technique we'll examine is linear regression, which generates a straight line to describe linear relationships. We'll start by examining the basic components of simple linear regression with one independent variable before discussing multiple regression with multiple independent variables.

Using the Seinfeld TV sitcom series as our data, let's start by plotting the two following variables, with season number as the x coordinate and the number of viewers per season (in millions) as the y coordinate.

Season (x)	Viewers (y)
1	19.22
2	18.07
3	17.67
4	20.52
5	29.59
6	31.27
7	33.19
8	32.24
9	38.11

Table 11: Seinfeld dataset

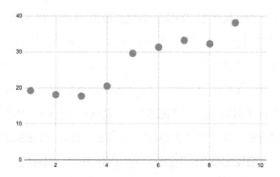

Figure 14: Seinfeld dataset plotted on a scatterplot

We can now see the dataset plotted on the scatterplot, with an upward trend in viewers starting at season 4 and the peak at season 9.

Let's next define the independent and dependent variables. For this example, we'll use the number of viewers per season as the dependent variable (what we want to predict) and the season number as the independent variable.

Using simple linear regression, let's now insert a straight line to describe the upward linear trend of our small dataset.

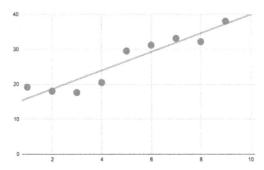

Figure 15: Linear regression hyperplane

As shown in Figure 15, this regression line neatly dissects the full company of data points. The technical term for the regression line is the *hyperplane*, and you'll see this term used throughout your study of machine learning. In a two-dimensional space, a hyperplane serves as a (flat) trendline, which is how Google Sheets titles linear regression in their scatterplot customization menu.

The goal of linear regression is to split the data in a way that minimizes the distance between the hyperplane and the observed values. This means that if you were to draw a vertical line from the hyperplane to each data point on the plot, the aggregate distance of each point would equate to the smallest possible distance to the hyperplane. The distance between the best fit line and the observed values is called the residual or error and the closer those values are to the hyperplane, the more accurate the model's predictions.

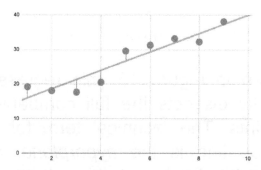

Figure 16: Error is the distance between the hyperplane and the observed value

The Slope

An important part of linear regression is the *slope*, which can be conveniently calculated by referencing the hyperplane. As one variable increases, the other variable will increase by the average value denoted by the hyperplane. The slope is therefore helpful for formulating predictions, such as predicting the number of season viewers for a potential tenth season of Seinfeld. Using the slope, we can input 10 as the x coordinate and find the corresponding y value, which in this case, is approximately 40 million viewers.

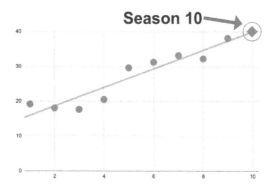

Figure 17: Using the slope/hyperplane to make a prediction

While linear regression isn't a fail-proof method for predicting trends, the trendline does offer a basic reference point for predicting unknown or future events.

Linear Regression Formula

The formula[17] for linear regression is y = bx + a.

"y" represents the dependent variable and "x" represents the independent variable.

"a" is the point where the hyperplane crosses the y-axis, known as the *y-intercept* or the value of y when x = 0.

"b" dictates the steepness of the slope and explains the relationship between x and y (what change in y is predicted for 1 unit change in x).

Calculation Example

Although your programming language takes care of this automatically, it's interesting to know how simple linear regression works. We'll use the following dataset to break down the formula.

	(X)	(Y)	XY	X^2
1	1	3	3	1
2	2	4	8	4
3	1	2	2	1
4	4	7	28	16
5	3	5	15	9
Σ (Total)	11	21	56	31

Table 12: Sample dataset
The final two columns of the table are not part of the original dataset and have been added for reference to complete the following formula.

$$a = \frac{(\Sigma y)(\Sigma x^2) - (\Sigma x)(\Sigma xy)}{n(\Sigma x^2) - (\Sigma x)^2}$$

$$b = \frac{n(\Sigma xy) - (\Sigma x)(\Sigma y)}{n(\Sigma x^2) - (\Sigma x)^2}$$

Where:

Σ = Total sum

Σx = Total sum of all x values (1 + 2 + 1 + 4 + 3 = 11)

Σy = Total sum of all y values (3 + 4 + 2 + 7 + 5 = 21)

Σxy = Total sum of x*y for each row (3 + 8 + 2 + 28 + 15 = 56)

Σx^2 = Total sum of x*x for each row (1 + 4 + 1 + 16 + 9 = 31)

n = Total number of rows. In the case of this example, n is equal to 5.

$$a = \frac{(\Sigma y)(\Sigma x^2) - (\Sigma x)(\Sigma xy)}{n(\Sigma x^2) - (\Sigma x)^2} \qquad a = \frac{(21)(31) - (11)(56)}{5(31) - (11)^2}$$

$$b = \frac{n(\Sigma xy) - (\Sigma x)(\Sigma y)}{n(\Sigma x^2) - (\Sigma x)^2} \qquad b = \frac{5(56) - (11)(21)}{5(31) - (11)^2}$$

a =

$((21 \times 31) - (11 \times 56)) / (5(31) - 11^2)$

$(651 - 616) / (155 - 121)$

$35 / 34 = 1.029$

b =

$(5(56) - (11 \times 21)) / (5(31) - 11^2)$
$(280 - 231) / (155 - 121)$
$49 / 34 = 1.441$

Insert the "a" and "b" values into the linear formula.

$y = bx + a$

$y = 1.441x + 1.029$

The linear formula $y = 1.441x + 1.029$ dictates how to draw the hyperplane.

Let's now test the linear regression model by looking up the coordinates for $x = 2$.

$y = 1.441(x) + 1.029$

$y = 1.441(2) + 1.029$

$y = 3.911$

In this case, the prediction is very close to the actual result of 4.0.

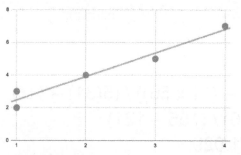

Figure 18: $y = 1.441x + 1.029$ plotted on the scatterplot

Multiple Linear Regression

Having summarized simple linear regression using a single independent variable, we can now look at multiple linear regression. This second technique is more applicable to machine learning given organizations use more than one independent variable to make decisions.

Multiple linear regression is simple linear regression but with more than one independent variable as the following formula shows.

$$y = a + b_1x_1 + b_2x_2 + b_3x_3 + \ldots$$

The y-intercept is still expressed as a, but now there are multiple independent variables (represented as x_1, x_2, x_3, etc.) and each with their own respected coefficient (b_1, b_2, b_3, etc).

As with simple linear regression, various sums of X and y values (including squared values) from the training data are used to solve for a (y-intercept) and b (coefficient values).

Once a model has been built using the X and y values from the training data, the multiple linear regression formula can be used to make a prediction (y) using the X values from the test data (to assess accuracy).

Discrete Variables

While the output (dependent variable) of linear regression must be continuous in the form of a floating-point or integer (whole number) value, the input (independent variables) can be continuous or categorical. For categorical variables, i.e. gender, these variables must be expressed numerically using one-hot encoding (0 or 1) and not as a string of letters (male, female).

Variable Selection

Before finishing this chapter, it's important to address the dilemma of variable selection and choosing an appropriate number of independent variables. On the one hand, adding more variables helps to account for more potential factors that control patterns in the data. On the other hand, this rationale only holds if the variables are relevant and possess some correlation/linear relationship with the dependent variable.

The expansion of independent variables also creates more relationships to consider. In simple linear regression, we saw a one-to-one relationship between two variables, whereas in multiple linear regression there is a many-to-one relationship. In multiple linear regression, not only are the independent variables potentially related to the dependent variable, but they are also potentially related to each other.

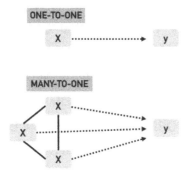

Figure 19: Simple linear regression (above) and multiple linear regression (below)

If a strong linear correlation exists between two independent variables, this can lead to a problem called multi-collinearity. When two independent variables are strongly correlated, they have a tendency to cancel each other out and provide the model with little to no unique information.

An example of two multi-collinear variables are liters of fuel consumed and liters of fuel in the tank to predict how far a jet plane will fly. Both independent variables are directly correlated, and in this case negatively correlated; as one variables increases, the other variable decreases and vice versa. When both variables are used to predict the dependent variable of how far the jet will fly, one effectively cancels the other out. It's still worthwhile to include one of these variables in the model, but it would be redundant to include both variables.

To avoid multi-collinearity, we need to check the relationship between each combination of independent variables using a scatterplot, pairplot (a matrix of relationships between variables), or correlation score.

If we look at the pairplot in Figure 20, we can analyze the relationship between all three variables (total_bill, tip, and size). If we set tip as the dependent variable, then we need to assess whether the two independent variables (total_bill and size) are strongly correlated. Using our pairplot, we can see there are two scatterplots visualizing the relationship between total_bill and size (row 1 on the right, and row 3 on the left). These two plots are not identical (as the x- and y-axis are inverted), but you can refer to either one.

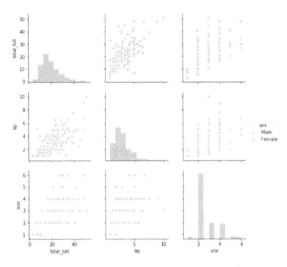

Figure 20: Pairplot with three variables

Judging by the upward linear trend, we can see that these two variables are partly correlated. However, if we were to insert a linear regression hyperplane, there would be significant residuals/error on both sides of the hyperplane to confirm that these two variables aren't strongly or directly correlated and we can definitely include both these variables in our regression model.

The following heatmap, shown in Figure 21, also confirms a modest correlation score of 0.6 between total_bill and size.

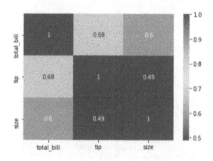

Figure 21: Heatmap with three variables

We can also use a pairplot, heatmap or correlation score to check if the independent variables are correlated to the dependent variable (and therefore relevant to the prediction outcome). In Figure 21, we can see that total_bill (0.68) and size (0.49) show some correlation with the dependent variable of tip. (Correlation is measured between -1 and 1, with a correlation of 1 describing a perfect positive relationship and a correlation of -1 indicating a perfect negative relationship. A coefficient of 0, meanwhile, denotes no relationship between two variables.)

In summary, the objective of multiple linear regression is for all the independent variables to be correlated with the dependent variable but not with each other.

CHAPTER QUIZ

Using **multiple linear regression**, your task is to create a model to predict the tip amount guests will leave the restaurant when paying for their meal. Note that this is a snippet of the actual dataset and the full dataset has 244 rows (diners).

	total_bill	tip	sex	smoker	day	time	size
0	16.99	1.01	Female	No	Sun	Dinner	2
1	10.34	1.66	Male	No	Sun	Dinner	3
2	21.01	3.50	Male	No	Sun	Dinner	3
3	23.68	3.31	Male	No	Sun	Dinner	2
4	24.59	3.61	Female	No	Sun	Dinner	4
5	25.29	4.71	Male	No	Sun	Dinner	4
6	8.77	2.00	Male	No	Sun	Dinner	2
7	26.88	3.12	Male	No	Sun	Dinner	4
8	15.04	1.96	Male	No	Sun	Dinner	2
9	14.78	3.23	Male	No	Sun	Dinner	2

1) **The dependent variable for this model should be which variable?**
   A) size
   B) total_bill and tip
   C) total_bill
   D) tip

2) From looking only at the data preview above, which variable(s) appear to have a linear relationship with total_bill?
A) smoker
B) total_bill and size
C) time
D) sex

3) It's important for the independent variables to be strongly correlated with the dependent variable and one or more of the other independent variables. True or False?

ANSWERS

1) D, tip

2) B, total_bill and size

(When there is an increase in both of these variables, we see a general increase in the tip for most rows. Other variables might be correlated to tip, but it's not clear to judge using only these 10 rows.)

3) False

(Ideally, the independent variables should not be strongly correlated with each other.)

## 8

LOGISTIC REGRESSION

As demonstrated in the previous chapter, linear regression is useful for quantifying relationships between variables to predict a continuous outcome. Total bill and size (number of guests) are both examples of continuous variables.

However, what if we want to predict a categorical variable such as "new customer" or "returning customer"? Unlike linear regression, the dependent variable (y) is no longer a continuous variable (such as total tip) but rather a discrete categorical variable.

Rather than quantify the linear relationship between variables, we need to use a classification technique such as logistic regression.

Logistic regression is still a supervised learning technique but produces a qualitative prediction rather than a quantitative prediction. This algorithm is often used to predict two discrete

classes, e.g., *pregnant* or *not pregnant.*
Given its strength in binary classification, logistic regression is used in many fields including fraud detection, disease diagnosis, emergency detection, loan default detection, or to identify spam email through the process of discerning specific classes, e.g., non-spam and spam.

Using the sigmoid function, logistic regression finds the probability of independent variables (X) producing a discrete dependent variable (y) such as "spam" or "non-spam."

$$y = \frac{1}{1+e^{-x}}$$

Where:

x = the independent variable you wish to transform

e = Euler's constant, 2.718

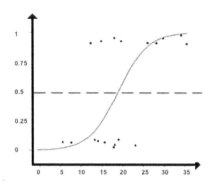

Figure 22: A sigmoid function used to classify data points

The sigmoid function produces an S-shaped curve that can convert any number and map it into a numerical value between 0 and 1 but without ever reaching those exact limits. Applying this formula, the sigmoid function converts independent variables into an expression of probability between 0 and 1 in relation to the dependent variable. In a binary case, a value of 0 represents no chance of occurring, and 1 represents a certain chance of occurring. The degree of probability for values located between 0 and 1 can be found according to how close they rest to 0 (impossible) or 1 (certain possibility).

Based on the found probabilities of the independent variables, logistic regression assigns each data point to a discrete class. In the case of binary classification (shown in Figure 22), the cut-off line to classify data points is 0.5. Data points that record a value above 0.5 are classified as Class A, and data points below 0.5 are classified as Class B. Data points that record a result of precisely 0.5 are unclassifiable but such instances are rare due to the mathematical component of the sigmoid function.

Following the logistic transformation using the Sigmoid function, the data points are assigned to one of two classes as presented in Figure 23.

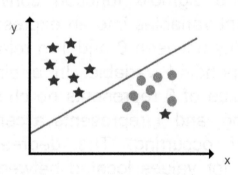

Figure 23: An example of logistic regression

Similar to linear regression. the independent variables, used as input to predict the dependent variable, can be categorical or continuous as long as they are expressed as numbers and not as strings of letters. In the case of discrete categorical variables, this involves using one-hot encoding to create a new set of variables to represent the original variable numerically.

Although logistic regression shares a visual resemblance to linear regression, the logistic hyperplane represents a classification/decision boundary rather than a prediction trendline. Thus, instead of using the hyperplane to make numeric predictions, the hyperplane is used to divide the dataset into classes.

The other distinction between logistic and linear regression is that the dependent variable (y) isn't placed along the y-axis in logistic regression. Instead, independent variables can be plotted along both axes, and the class (output) of the dependent variable is determined by the position of the data point in relation to the decision boundary. Data points on one side of the decision boundary are classified as Class A, and data points on the opposing side of the decision boundary are Class B.

For classification scenarios with more than two possible discrete outcomes, multinomial logistic regression can be used as shown in Figure 24.

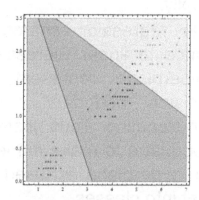

Figure 24: An example of multinomial logistic regression

As a similar classification method, multinomial logistic regression solves multiclass problems with more than two possible discrete outcomes. Multinomial logistic regression can also be applied to ordinal cases where there are a set number of discrete outcomes, e.g., pre-undergraduate, undergraduate, and postgraduate. Keep in mind, though, that logistic regression's core strength lies in binary prediction, and other classification algorithms including decision trees or support vector machines may be a better option for solving multiclass problems.

Two tips to remember when using logistic regression are that the dataset should be free of missing values and that all independent variables are independent and not strongly correlated with each other. There should also be sufficient data for each output variable to ensure high accuracy. A good starting point would be approximately 30-50 data points for each output, i.e., 60-100 total data points for binary logistic regression. In general, logistic regression normally doesn't work so well with large datasets, and especially messy data containing outliers, complex relationships, and missing values.

If you would like to learn more about the mathematical foundation of logistic regression, you can check out *Statistics 101: Logistic Regression* series on YouTube by Brandon Foltz.[18]

CHAPTER QUIZ

Using **logistic regression**, your task is to classify penguins into different classes based on the following dataset. Please note that this dataset has 344 rows and the following screenshot is a snippet of the full dataset.

	species	island	bill_length_mm	bill_depth_mm	flipper_length_mm	body_mass_g	sex
0	Adelie	Torgersen	39.1	18.7	181.0	3750.0	MALE
1	Adelie	Torgersen	39.5	17.4	186.0	3800.0	FEMALE
2	Adelie	Torgersen	40.3	18.0	195.0	3250.0	FEMALE
3	Adelie	Torgersen	NaN	NaN	NaN	NaN	NaN
4	Adelie	Torgersen	36.7	19.3	193.0	3450.0	FEMALE
5	Adelie	Torgersen	39.3	20.6	190.0	3650.0	MALE
6	Adelie	Torgersen	38.9	17.8	181.0	3625.0	FEMALE
7	Adelie	Torgersen	39.2	19.6	195.0	4675.0	MALE
8	Adelie	Torgersen	34.1	18.1	193.0	3475.0	NaN
9	Adelie	Torgersen	42.0	20.2	190.0	4250.0	NaN

1)   Which three variables (in their current form) could we use as the dependent variable to classify penguins?

2)   Which row(s) contains missing values?

3) Which variable in the dataset preview is binary?

ANSWERS

1) species, island, or sex

2) Row 3, 8, and 9

(NaN = missing value)

3) sex

(Species and island might also be binary but we can't judge from the screenshot alone.)

k-NEAREST NEIGHBORS

Another popular classification technique in machine learning is *k*-nearest neighbors (*k*-NN). As a supervised learning algorithm, *k*-NN classifies new data points based on their position to nearby data points.

In many ways, *k*-NN is similar to a voting system or a popularity contest. Imagine you're the new kid at school and you need to know how to dress in order to fit in with the rest of the class. On your first day at school, you see six of the nine students sitting closest to you with their sleeves rolled-up. Based on numerical supremacy and close proximity, the following day you also make the decision to roll up your sleeves.

Let's now look at another example.

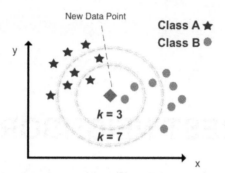

Figure 25: An example of k-NN clustering used to predict the class of a new data point

Here in Figure 25, the data points have been classified into two classes, and a new data point, whose class is unknown, is added to the plot. Using k-NN, we can predict the category of the new data point based on its position to the existing data points.

First, though, we need to set "k" to determine how many data points we want to use to classify the new data point. If we set k to 3, k-NN analyzes the new data point's position in respect to the three nearest data points (neighbors). The outcome of selecting the three closest neighbors returns two Class B data points and one Class A data point. Defined by k (3), the model's prediction for determining the category of the new data point is Class B as it returns two out of the three nearest neighbors.

The chosen number of neighbors identified, defined by k, is crucial in determining the results. In Figure 25, you can see that the outcome of classification changes by altering k from "3" to "7." It's therefore useful to test numerous k combinations to find the best fit and avoid setting k too low or too high. Setting k too low will increase bias and lead to misclassification and setting k too high will make it computationally expensive. Setting k to an uneven number will also help to eliminate the possibility of a statistical stalemate and an invalid result. Five is the default number of neighbors for this algorithm using Scikit-learn.

Given that the scale of the individual variables has a major impact on the output of k-NN, the dataset usually needs to be scaled to standardize variance as discussed in Chapter 5. This transformation will help to avoid one or more variables with a high range unfairly pulling the focus of the k-NN model.

In regards to what type of data to use with k-NN, this algorithm works best with continuous variables. It is still possible to use binary categorical variables represented as 0 and 1, but the results are more likely to be informed by the binary splits relative to the dispersion across other variables as visualized in Figure 26.

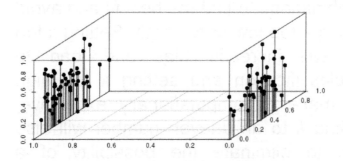

Figure 26: One binary variable and two continuous variables

Above, we can see that the horizontal x-axis is binary (0 or 1), which splits the data into two distinct sides. Moreover, if we switch one of the existing continuous variables to a binary variable (as shown in Figure 27), we can see that the distance between variables is influenced even more greatly by the outcome of the binary variables.

If you do wish to examine binary variables, it's therefore best to only include critical binary variables for *k*-NN analysis.

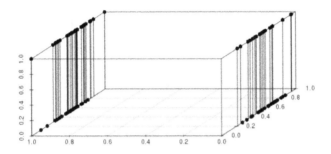

Figure 27: Two binary variable and one continuous variable

While *k*-NN is generally accurate and easy to comprehend, storing an entire dataset and calculating the distance between each new data point and all existing data points puts a heavy burden on computing resources. This means that the number of data points in the dataset is proportional to the time it takes to execute a single prediction, which can lead to slower processing times. For this reason, *k*-NN is generally not recommended for analyzing large datasets.

Another downside is that it can be challenging to apply *k*-NN to high-dimensional data with a high number of features. Measuring multiple distances between data points in a high-dimensional space is also taxing on computing resources and it becomes more difficult to perform accurate classification.

CHAPTER QUIZ

Your task is to classify penguins into different species using the **k-nearest neighbors** algorithm, with *k* set to 5 (neighbors). Please note that this dataset has 344 rows and the following is a preview of the full dataset.

	species	bill_length_mm	bill_depth_mm	flipper_length_mm	body_mass_g	sex
0	Adelie	39.1	18.7	181.0	3750.0	MALE
1	Adelie	39.5	17.4	186.0	3800.0	FEMALE
2	Adelie	40.3	18.0	195.0	3250.0	FEMALE
3	Adelie	NaN	NaN	NaN	NaN	NaN
4	Adelie	36.7	19.3	193.0	3450.0	FEMALE
5	Adelie	39.3	20.6	190.0	3650.0	MALE
6	Adelie	38.9	17.8	181.0	3625.0	FEMALE
7	Adelie	39.2	19.6	195.0	4675.0	MALE
8	Adelie	34.1	18.1	193.0	3475.0	NaN
9	Adelie	42.0	20.2	190.0	4250.0	NaN

1) Which of the following variables should we consider removing from our *k*-NN model?
A. sex
B. species
C. body_mass_g
D. bill_depth_mm

2) If we wanted to reduce the processing time of our model, which

of the following methods is recommended?

A. Increase *k* from 5 to 10
B. Reduce *k* from 10 to 5
C. Re-run the model and hope for a faster result
D. Increase the size of the training data

3) To include the variable 'sex' in our model, which data scrubbing technique do we need to use?

ANSWERS

1) A, sex

(Binary variables should only be used when critical to the model's accuracy.)

2) B, Reduce k from 10 to 5

3) One-hot encoding (to convert the variable into a numerical identifier of 0 or 1)

k-MEANS CLUSTERING

The next method of analysis involves grouping or clustering data points that share similar attributes using unsupervised learning. An online business, for example, wants to examine a segment of customers that purchase at the same time of the year and discern what factors influence their purchasing behavior. By understanding a given cluster of customers, they can then form decisions regarding which products to recommend to customer groups using promotions and personalized offers. Outside of market research, clustering can also be applied to other scenarios, including pattern recognition, fraud detection, and image processing.

One of the most popular clustering techniques is *k*-means clustering. As an unsupervised learning algorithm, k-means clustering attempts to divide data into k number of discrete groups and is highly effective at uncovering new patterns. Examples of potential groupings include animal species, customers with similar features, and housing market segmentation.

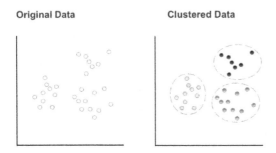

Figure 28: Comparison of original data and clustered data using k-means

The k-means clustering algorithm works by first splitting data into k number of clusters, with k representing the number of clusters you wish to create. If you choose to split your dataset into three clusters, for example, then k should be set to 3. In Figure 28, we can see that the original data has been transformed into three clusters (k = 3). If we were to set k to 4, an additional cluster would be derived from the dataset to produce four clusters.

How does *k*-means clustering separate the data points? The first step is to examine the unclustered data and manually select a centroid for each cluster. That centroid then forms the epicenter of an individual cluster.

Centroids can be chosen at random, which means you can nominate any data point on the scatterplot to act as a centroid. However, you can save time by selecting centroids dispersed across the scatterplot and not directly adjacent to each other. In other words, start by guessing where you think the centroids for each cluster might be positioned. The remaining data points on the scatterplot are then assigned to the nearest centroid by measuring the Euclidean distance.

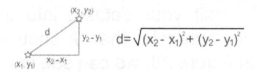

Figure 29: Calculating Euclidean distance

Each data point can be assigned to only one cluster, and each cluster is discrete.

This means that there's no overlap between clusters and no case of nesting a cluster inside another cluster. Also, all data points, including anomalies, are assigned to a centroid irrespective of how they impact the final shape of the cluster. However, due to the statistical force that pulls nearby data points to a central point, clusters will typically form an elliptical or spherical shape.

After all data points have been allocated to a centroid, the next step is to aggregate the mean value of the data points in each cluster, which can be found by calculating the average x and y values of the data points contained in each cluster.

Next, take the mean value of the data points in each cluster and plug in those x and y values to update your centroid coordinates. This will most likely result in one or more changes to the location of your centroid(s). The total number of clusters, however, remains the same as you are not creating new clusters but rather updating their position on the scatterplot. Like musical chairs, the remaining data points rush to the closest centroid to form *k* number of clusters.

Should any data point on the scatterplot switch clusters with the changing of centroids, the previous step is repeated. This means, again, calculating the average mean value of the cluster and updating the x and y values of each centroid to reflect the average coordinates of the data points in that cluster.

Once you reach a stage where the data points no longer switch clusters after an update in centroid coordinates, the algorithm is complete, and you have your final set of clusters.

The following diagrams break down the full algorithmic process.

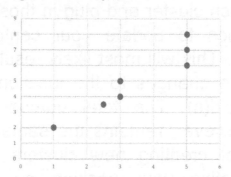

Figure 30: Sample data points are plotted on a scatterplot

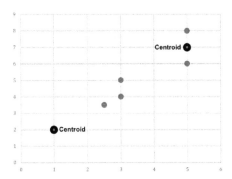

Figure 31: Two existing data points are nominated as the centroids

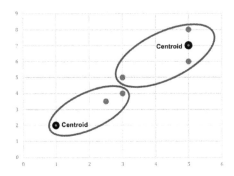

Figure 32: Two clusters are formed after calculating the Euclidean distance of the remaining data points to the centroids.

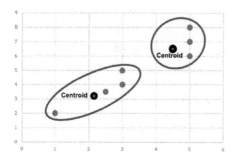

Figure 33: The centroid coordinates for each cluster are updated to reflect the cluster's mean value. The two previous centroids stay in their original position and two new centroids are added to the scatterplot. Lastly, as one data point has switched from the right cluster to the left cluster, the centroids of both clusters need to be updated one last time.

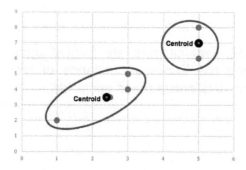

Figure 34: Two final clusters are produced based on the updated centroids for each cluster

For this example, it took two iterations to successfully create our two clusters. However, *k*-means clustering is not always able to reliably identify a final combination of clusters. In such cases, you will need to switch tactics and utilize another algorithm to formulate your classification model.

Also, be aware that you may need to rescale the input features using standardization before running the *k*-means algorithm. This will help to preserve the true shape of the clusters and avoid exaggerated variance from affecting the final output (i.e. over-stretched clusters).

Setting *k*

When setting "*k*" for *k*-means clustering, it's important to find the right number of clusters. In general, as *k* increases, clusters become smaller and variance falls. However, the downside is that neighboring clusters become less distinct from one another as *k* increases. If you set *k* to the same number of data points in your dataset, each data point automatically becomes a standalone cluster. Conversely, if you set k to 1, then all data points will be deemed as homogenous and fall inside one large cluster. Needless to say, setting k to either extreme does not provide any worthwhile insight.

In order to optimize k, you may wish to use a scree plot for guidance. A scree plot charts the degree of scattering (variance) inside a cluster as the total number of clusters increase. Scree plots are famous for their iconic "elbow," which reflects several pronounced kinks in the plot's curve. A scree plot compares the Sum of Squared Error (SSE) for each variation of total clusters. SSE is measured as the sum of the squared distance between the centroid and the other neighbors inside the cluster. In a nutshell, SSE drops as more clusters are produced.

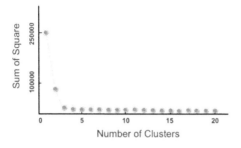

Figure 35: A scree plot

This begs the question of what's an optimal number of clusters? In general, you should opt for a cluster solution where SSE subsides dramatically to the left on the scree plot but before it reaches a point of negligible change with cluster variations to its right. For instance, in Figure 35, there is little change in SSE for four or more clusters. This would result in clusters that would be small and difficult to distinguish.

In this scree plot, two or three clusters appear to be an ideal solution. There exists a significant kink to the left of these two cluster variations due to a pronounced drop-off in SSE. Meanwhile, there is still some change in SSE with the solution to their right. This will ensure that these two cluster solutions are distinct and have an impact on data classification.

Another useful technique to decide the number of cluster solutions is to divide the total number of data points (n) by two and finding the square root.

$$\sqrt{\frac{n}{2}}$$

If we have 200 data points, for example, the recommended number of clusters is 10, whereas if we have 18 data points, the suggested number of clusters is 3.

A more simple and non-mathematical approach to setting k is to apply domain knowledge. I might want to set k to 2, for example, if I am analyzing data about visitors to the website of a major IT provider. Why two clusters? Because I already know there is a significant discrepancy in spending behavior between returning visitors and new visitors. First-time visitors rarely purchase enterprise-level IT products and services, as these customers usually go through a lengthy research and vetting process before procurement can be approved.

Based on this knowledge, I can use *k*-means clustering to create two clusters and test my hypothesis. After producing two clusters, I may then choose to examine one of the two clusters further, by either applying another technique or again using *k*-means clustering. For instance, I might want to split the returning users into two clusters (using *k*-means clustering) to test my hypothesis that mobile users and desktop users produce two disparate groups of data points. Again, by applying domain knowledge, I know it's uncommon for large enterprises to make big-ticket purchases on a mobile device and I can test this assumption using *k*-means clustering.

If, though, I am analyzing a product page for a low-cost item, such as a $4.99 domain name, new visitors and returning visitors are less likely to produce two distinct clusters. As the item price is low, new users are less likely to deliberate before purchasing. Instead, I might choose to set *k* to 3 based on my three primary lead generators: organic traffic, paid traffic, and email marketing. These three lead sources are likely to produce three discrete clusters based on the fact that:

a)   **Organic traffic** generally consists of both new and returning customers with the intention to purchase from my website (through pre-selection, e.g., word of mouth, previous customer experience).

b)   **Paid traffic** targets new customers who typically arrive on the site with a lower level of trust than organic traffic, including potential customers who click on the paid advertisement by mistake.

c)   **Email marketing** reaches existing customers who already have experience purchasing from the website and have established and verified user accounts.

This is an example of domain knowledge based on my occupation but understand that the effectiveness of "domain knowledge" diminishes dramatically past a low number of k clusters. In other words, domain knowledge might be sufficient for determining two to four clusters but less valuable when choosing between a higher number of clusters, such as 20 or 21 clusters.

CHAPTER QUIZ

Your task is to group the flights dataset (which tracks flights from 1949 to 1960) into discrete clusters using **k-means clustering**. The full dataset has 145 rows.

	year	month	passengers
0	1949	January	112
1	1949	February	118
2	1949	March	132
3	1949	April	129
4	1949	May	121
5	1949	June	135
6	1949	July	148
7	1949	August	148
8	1949	September	136
9	1949	October	119

1)   Using *k*-means clustering to analyze all 3 variables, what might be a good initial number of *k* clusters (using only domain/general knowledge) to train the model?

        A. $k = 2$

B. $k = 100$
C. $k = 12$
D. $k = 3$

2) What mathematical technique might we use to find the appropriate number of clusters?
A. Big elbow method
B. Mean absolute error
C. Scree plot
D. One-hot encoding

3) Which variable requires data scrubbing?

ANSWERS

1) 12

(Given there are 12 months in a year, there may be some reoccurring patterns in regards to the number of passengers flying each month.)

2) C, Scree plot

3) Month

(This variable needs to be converted into a numerical identifier in order to measure its distance to other variables.)

BIAS & VARIANCE

Algorithm selection is an essential step in understanding patterns in your data but designing a generalized model that accurately predicts new data points can be a challenging task. The fact that most algorithms have many different hyperparameters also leads to a vast number of potential outcomes.

As a quick recap, hyperparameters are lines of code that act as the algorithm's settings, similar to the controls on the dashboard of an airplane or knobs used to tune radio frequency.

```
model = ensemble.GradientBoostingRegressor(
    n_estimators=150,
    learning_rate=0.1,
    max_depth=4,
    min_samples_split=4,
    min_samples_leaf=4,
    max_features=0.5,
    loss='huber'
)
```

Figure 36: Example of hyperparameters in Python for the algorithm gradient boosting

A constant challenge in machine learning is navigating *underfitting* and *overfitting*, which describe how closely your model follows the actual patterns of the data. To comprehend underfitting and overfitting, you must first understand *bias* and *variance*.

Bias refers to the gap between the value predicted by your model and the actual value of the data. In the case of high bias, your predictions are likely to be skewed in a particular direction away from the true values. Variance describes how scattered your predicted values are in relation to each other. Bias and variance can be better understood by viewing the following visual representation.

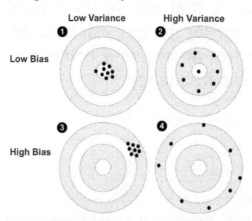

Figure 37: Shooting targets used to represent bias and variance

Shooting targets, as seen in Figure 37, are not a visualization technique used in machine learning but can be used here to explain bias and variance.[19]

Imagine that the center of the target, or the bull's-eye, perfectly predicts the correct value of your data. The dots marked on the target represent an individual prediction of your model based on the training or test data provided. In certain cases, the dots will be densely positioned close to the bull's-eye, ensuring that predictions made by the model are close to the actual values and patterns found in the data. In other cases, the model's predictions will lie more scattered across the target. The more the predictions deviate from the bull's-eye, the higher the bias and the less reliable your model is at making accurate predictions.

In the first target, we can see an example of low bias and low variance. The bias is low because the model's predictions are closely aligned to the center, and there is low variance because the predictions are positioned densely in one general location.

The second target (located on the right of the first row) shows a case of low bias and high variance. Although the predictions are not as close to the bull's-eye as the previous example, they are still near to the center, and the bias is therefore relatively low. However, there is a high variance this time because the predictions are spread out from each other.

The third target (located on the left of the second row) represents high bias and low variance and the fourth target (located on the right of the second row) shows high bias and high variance.

Ideally, you want a situation where there's both low variance and low bias. In reality, however, there's a trade-off between optimal bias and optimal variance. Bias and variance both contribute to error but it's the prediction error that you want to minimize, not the bias or variance specifically.

Like learning to ride a bicycle for the first time, finding an optimal balance is one of the more challenging aspects of machine learning. Peddling algorithms through the data is the easy part; the hard part is navigating bias and variance while maintaining a state of balance in your model.

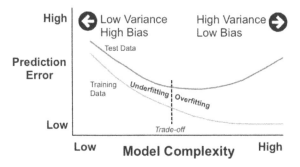

Figure 38: Model complexity based on the prediction error

Let's explore this problem further using a visual example. In Figure 38, we can see two curves. The upper curve represents the test data, and the lower curve depicts the training data. From the left, both curves begin at a point of high prediction error due to low variance and high bias. As they move toward the right, they change to the opposite: high variance and low bias. This leads to low prediction error in the case of the training data and high prediction error in the case of the test data. In the middle of the plot is an optimal balance of prediction error between the training and test data. This midground is a typical illustration of the bias-variance trade-off.

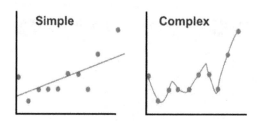

Figure 39: Underfitting on the left and overfitting on the right

Mismanaging the bias-variance trade-off can lead to poor results. As seen in Figure 39, this can result in the model being overly simple and inflexible (underfitting) or overly complex and flexible (overfitting).

Underfitting (low variance, high bias) on the left and overfitting (high variance, low bias) on the right are shown in these two scatterplots. A natural temptation is to add complexity to the model (as shown on the right) to improve accuracy, but this can, in turn, lead to overfitting. An overfitted model yields accurate predictions using the training data but is less precise at making predictions using the test data. Overfitting can also occur if the training and test data aren't randomized before they are split and patterns in the data aren't distributed evenly across the two segments of data.

Underfitting is when your model is overly simple, and again, has not scratched the surface of the underlying patterns in the data. This can lead to inaccurate predictions for both the training data and test data. Common causes of underfitting include insufficient training data to adequately cover all possible combinations, and situations where the training and test data weren't properly randomized.

To mitigate underfitting and overfitting, you may need to modify the model's hyperparameters to ensure that they fit the patterns of both the training and test data and not just one split of the data. A suitable fit should acknowledge significant trends in the data and play down or even omit minor variations. This might mean re-randomizing your training and test data, adding new data points to better detect underlying patterns or switching algorithms to manage the issue of the bias-variance trade-off. Linear regression, for example, is one learning algorithm that rarely encounters overfitting (but may be susceptible to underfitting).

Switching from linear regression to non-linear regression can also reduce bias by increasing variance. Alternatively, increasing "k" in k-NN minimizes variance (by averaging together more neighbors). A third example could be reducing variance by switching from a single decision tree (which is prone to overfitting) to random forests with many decision trees.

An advanced strategy to combat overfitting is to introduce *regularization*, which reduces the risk of overfitting by constraining the model to make it simpler. In effect, this add-on hyperparameter artificially amplifies bias error by penalizing an increase in a model's complexity and provides a warning alert to keep high variance in check while other hyperparameters are being tested and optimized.

Setting the regularization hyperparameter to a high value will avoid overfitting the model to the training data but may lead to some underfitting. In linear regression, this would constitute a relatively flat slope (close to zero) for the hyperplane or an overly wide margin in the case of support vector machines.

Lastly, one other technique to improve model accuracy is to perform cross validation, as covered earlier in Chapter 6, to minimize pattern discrepancies between the training data and the test data.

SUPPORT VECTOR MACHINES

Developed inside the computer science community in the 1990s, support vector machines (SVM) was initially designed for predicting numeric and categorical outcomes as a double-barrel prediction technique. Today, though, SVM is mostly used as a classification technique for predicting categorical outcomes.

As a classification technique, SVM is similar to logistic regression, in that it's used to filter data into a binary or multiclass target variable. But, as seen in Figure 40, SVM sets a different emphasis on the location of the classification boundary line.

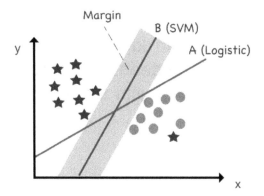

Figure 40: Logistic regression versus SVM

The scatterplot in Figure 40 consists of 17 data points that are linearly separable. We can see that the logistic decision boundary (A) splits the data points into two classes in a way that minimizes the distance between all data points and the decision boundary. The second line, the SVM boundary (B), also separates the two classes but it does so from a position of maximum distance between itself and the two classes of data points.

You'll also notice a gray zone that denotes *margin*, which is the distance between the decision boundary and the nearest data point, multiplied by two. The margin is a key part of SVM and is important because it offers additional support to cope with new data points that may infringe on the decision boundary (as is the case with logistic regression). To illustrate this scenario, let's consider the same scatterplot with the inclusion of a new data point.

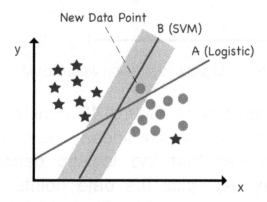

Figure 41: A new data point is added to the scatterplot

The new data point is a circle, but it's located incorrectly on the left side of the logistic (A) decision boundary (designated for stars). The new data point, though, remains correctly located on the right side of the SVM (B) decision boundary (designated for circles) courtesy of ample "support" supplied by the margin.

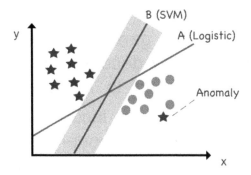

Figure 42: Mitigating anomalies

SVM is also useful for untangling complex relationships and mitigating outliers and anomalies. A limitation of standard logistic regression is that it goes out of its way to fit outliers and anomalies (as seen in the scatterplot with the star in the bottom right corner in Figure 42). SVM, however, is less sensitive to such data points and actually minimizes their impact on the final location of the boundary line. In Figure 42, we can see that Line B (SVM) is less sensitive to the anomalous star on the right-hand side. SVM can thus be used as a method for managing variant data.

The SVM boundary can also be modified to ignore misclassified cases in the training data using a hyperparameter called C. In machine learning, you typically want to generalize patterns rather than precisely decode the training data (which is bound to contain some degree of noise[20]) as incurring some mistakes in training the model may lead to a model that generalizes better on real data. There is therefore a trade-off in SVM between a **wide margin/more mistakes** and a **narrow margin/fewer mistakes**. The higher goal of your model is to strike a balance between "not too strict" and "not too loose", and, by modifying the C hyperparameter, you can regulate to what extent the misclassified cases (on the wrong side of the margin) are ignored.

Adding flexibility to the model using the hyperparameter C introduces what's called a "soft margin," which ignores a determined portion of cases that cross over the soft margin—leading to greater generalization in the model. The margin is made wider or soft when C is to set to a low value. A C value of '0,' meanwhile, enforces no penalty on misclassified cases. Conversely, a large C value[21] makes the cost of misclassification high, thereby narrowing the width of the margin (hard margin) to avoid misclassification. This may force the model to overfit the training data and thereby misclassify new data points.

You can combat overfitting—where the model performs well on the training data but not on new data—by reducing C as this adds regularization to the model. Finding an optimal C value is generally chosen experimentally based on trial and error, which can be automated using a technique called grid search (discussed in Chapter 18).

C = 0.8   C = 100

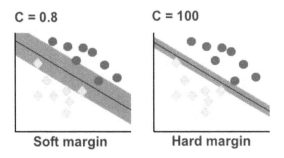

Soft margin   Hard margin

Figure 43: Soft margin versus hard margin

While the examples discussed so far have comprised two features plotted on a two-dimensional scatterplot, SVM's real strength lies with high-dimensional data and handling multiple features. SVM has numerous advanced variations available to classify high-dimensional data using what's called the Kernel Trick. This is an advanced solution to map data from a low-dimensional to a high-dimensional space when a dataset cannot be separated using a linear decision boundary in its original space. Transitioning from a two-dimensional to a three-dimensional space, for example, allows us to use a linear plane to split the data within a 3-D area. In other words, the kernel trick lets us classify data points with non-linear characteristics using linear classification in a higher dimension.

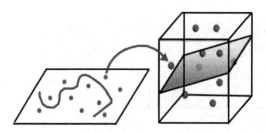

Figure 44: In this example, the decision boundary provides a non-linear separator between the data in a 2-D space but transforms into a linear separator between data points when projected into a 3-D space

A factor to be mindful of when using SVM is that it can be sensitive to feature scales and you may need to rescale the data prior to training.[22] Using standardization, you can convert the range of each feature to a standard normal distribution with a mean of zero. Standardization is implemented in Scikit-learn using StandardScaler. Documentation for StandardScaler can be found at http://bit.ly/378pf9Q.

Lastly, the processing time to train a model relative to logistic regression and other classification algorithms can be a drawback to using SVM. In particular, SVM is not recommended for datasets with a low feature-to-row ratio (low number of features relative to rows) due to speed and performance constraints. SVM does, though, excel at untangling outliers from complex small and medium-sized datasets and managing high-dimensional data.

CHAPTER QUIZ

Using an **SVM classifier**, your task is to classify which island a penguin has come from after arriving on your own island. To predict the island, you can use any or all of the variables from the penguin dataset.

	species	island	bill_length_mm	bill_depth_mm	flipper_length_mm	body_mass_g	sex
0	Adelie	Torgersen	39.1	18.7	181.0	3750.0	MALE
1	Adelie	Torgersen	39.5	17.4	186.0	3800.0	FEMALE
2	Adelie	Torgersen	40.3	18.0	195.0	3250.0	FEMALE
3	Adelie	Torgersen	NaN	NaN	NaN	NaN	NaN
4	Adelie	Torgersen	36.7	19.3	193.0	3450.0	FEMALE
5	Adelie	Torgersen	39.3	20.6	190.0	3650.0	MALE
6	Adelie	Torgersen	38.9	17.8	181.0	3625.0	FEMALE
7	Adelie	Torgersen	39.2	19.6	195.0	4675.0	MALE
8	Adelie	Torgersen	34.1	18.1	193.0	3475.0	NaN
9	Adelie	Torgersen	42.0	20.2	190.0	4250.0	NaN

1) **Which of the following variables would be the dependent variable for this model?**

A. island
B. species
C. sex
D. body_mass_g

2) Which of the following variables could we use as independent variable(s)?

A. island
B. All of the variables
C. All of the variables except island
D. species

3) What are two data scrubbing techniques commonly used with this algorithm?

ANSWERS

1) A, island

2) C, All of the variables except island

3) Regularization and standardization

ARTIFICIAL NEURAL NETWORKS

This penultimate chapter on machine learning algorithms brings us to artificial neural networks (ANN) and the gateway to reinforcement learning. Artificial neural networks, also known as *neural networks*, is a popular machine learning technique for analyzing data through a network of decision layers. The naming of this technique was inspired by the algorithm's structural resemblance to the human brain. While this doesn't mean artificial neural networks are a virtual reproduction of the brain's decision-making process, there does exist some general similarities.

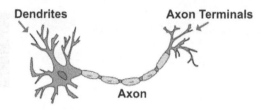

Figure 45: Anatomy of a human brain neuron

The brain, for example, contains interconnected neurons with dendrites that receive inputs. From these inputs, the neuron produces an electric signal output from the axon and emits these signals through axon terminals to other neurons. Similarly, artificial neural networks consist of interconnected decision functions, known as *nodes,* which interact with each other through axon-like *edges*.

The nodes of a neural network are separated into layers and generally start with a wide base. This first layer consists of raw input data (such as numeric values, text, image pixels or sound) divided into nodes. Each input node then sends information to the next layer of nodes via the network's edges.

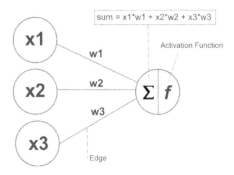

Figure 46: The nodes, edges/weights, and sum/activation function of a basic neural network

Each edge in the network has a numeric weight that can be altered based on experience. If the sum of the connected edges satisfies a set threshold, known as the *activation function*, this activates a neuron at the next layer. If the sum of the connected edges does not meet the set threshold, the activation function fails, which results in an *all or nothing* arrangement. Moreover, the weights assigned to each edge are unique, which means the nodes fire differently, preventing them from producing the same solution.

Using supervised learning, the model's predicted output is compared to the actual output (that's known to be correct), and the difference between these two results is measured as the *cost* or *cost value*. The purpose of training is to reduce the cost value until the model's prediction closely matches the correct output. This is achieved by incrementally tweaking the network's weights until the lowest possible cost value is obtained. This particular process of training the neural network is called *back-propagation*. Rather than navigate from left to right like how data is fed into the network, back-propagation rolls in reverse from the output layer on the right to the input layer on the left.

The Black-box Dilemma

One of the downsides of a network-based model is the black-box dilemma. Although the network can approximate accurate outputs, tracing its decision structure reveals limited to no insight about how specific variables influence its decision. For instance, if we use a neural network to predict the outcome of a Kickstarter campaign (an online funding platform for creative projects), the network can analyze numerous independent variables including campaign category, currency, deadline, and minimum pledge amount, etc. However, the model is unable to specify the relationship of these independent variables to the dependent variable of the campaign reaching its funding target. Algorithms such as decision trees and linear regression, meanwhile, are transparent as they show the variables' relationships to a given output. Moreover, it's possible for two neural networks with different topologies and weights to produce the same output, which makes it even more challenging to trace the impact of specific variables on the final output.

This begs the question of when should you use a neural network (given it's a black-box technique)? To answer this question, neural networks generally fit prediction tasks with a large number of input features and complex patterns, and especially problems that are difficult for computers to decipher but simple and almost trivial for humans. One example is the CAPTCHA (Completely Automated

Public Turing test to tell Computers and Humans Apart) challenge-response test on websites to determine whether a user is human. Another example is identifying if a pedestrian is preparing to step into the path of an oncoming vehicle. In both examples, obtaining a fast and accurate prediction is more important than decoding the specific variables and their relationship to the final output.

Building a Neural Network

A typical neural network can be divided into input, hidden, and output layers. Data is first received by the input layer, where features are detected. The hidden layer(s) then analyze and process the input features, and the final result is shown as the output layer.

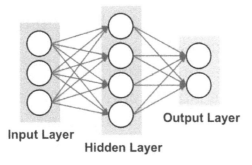

Input Layer

Hidden Layer

Output Layer

Figure 47: The three general layers of a neural network

The middle layers are considered hidden because, like human vision, they covertly process objects between the input and output layers. When faced with four lines connected in the shape of a square, our eyes instantly recognize those four lines as a square. We don't notice the mental processing that is involved to register the four polylines (input) as a square (output). Neural networks work in a similar way as they break data into layers and process the hidden layers to produce a final output. As more hidden layers are added to the network, the model's capacity to analyze complex patterns also improves. This is why models with a deep number of layers are often referred to as *deep learning*[23] to distinguish their deeper and superior processing abilities.

While there are many techniques to assemble the nodes of a neural network, the simplest method is the feed-forward network where signals flow only in one direction and there's no loop in the network. The most basic form of a feed-forward neural network is the *perceptron*, which was devised in the 1950s by Professor Frank Rosenblatt.

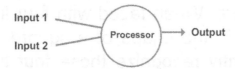

Figure 48: Visual representation of a perceptron neural network

The perceptron was designed as a decision function for receiving inputs to produce a binary output. Its structure consists of one or more inputs, a processor, and a single output. Inputs are fed into the processor (neuron), processed, and an output is then generated.

A perceptron supports one of two potential outputs, "0" or "1." An output of

"1" triggers the activation function, while "0" does not. When working with a larger neural network with additional layers, the "1" output can be configured to pass the output to the next layer. Conversely, "0" is configured to be ignored and is not passed to the next layer for processing.

As a supervised learning technique, the perceptron builds a prediction model based on these five steps:

1) Inputs are fed into the processor.
2) The perceptron applies weights to estimate the value of those inputs.
3) The perceptron computes the error between the estimate and the actual value.
4) The perceptron adjusts its weights according to the error.
5) These four steps are repeated until you are satisfied with the model's accuracy. The training model can then be applied to the test data.

To illustrate this process, let's say we have a perceptron consisting of two inputs:

Input 1: $x1 = 24$

Input 2: $x_2 = 16$

We then add a random weight to these two inputs, and they are sent to the neuron for processing.

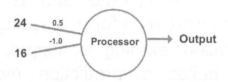

Figure 49: Weights are added to the perceptron

Weights
Input 1: 0.5
Input 2: -1

Next, we multiply each weight by its input:
Input 1: 24 * 0.5 = 12
Input 2: 16 * -1 = -16

Although the perceptron produces a binary output (0 or 1), there are many ways to configure the activation function. For this example, we will set the activation function to ≥ 0. This means that if the sum is a positive number or equal to zero, then the output is 1. Meanwhile, if the sum is a negative number, the output is 0.

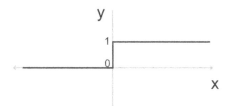

Figure 50: Activation function where the output (y) is 0 when x is negative, and the output (y) is 1 when x is positive

Thus:
Input 1: 24 * 0.5 = 12
Input 2: 16 * -1.0 = -16
Sum (Σ): 12 + -16 = -4

As a numeric value less than zero, the result produces "0" and does not trigger the perceptron's activation function. Given this error, the perceptron needs to adjust its weights in response.

Updated weights:
Input 1: 24 * 0.5 = 12
Input 2: 16 * -0.5 = -8
Sum (Σ): 12 + -16 = 4

As a positive outcome, the perceptron now produces "1" which triggers the activation function, and if in a larger network, this would trigger the next layer of analysis.

In this example, the activation function was ≥ 0. We could, though, modify the activation threshold to follow a different rule, such as:

$x > 3$, $y = 1$
$x \leq 3$, $y = 0$

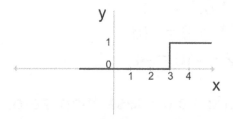

Figure 51: Activation function where the output (y) is 0 when x is equal to or less than 3, and the output (y) is 1 when x is greater than 3

A weakness of a perceptron is that because the output is binary (0 or 1), small changes in the weights or bias in any single perceptron within a larger neural network can induce polarizing results. This can lead to dramatic changes within the network and flip the final output, which makes it difficult to train a model that is accurate with new data.

An alternative to the perceptron is the *sigmoid neuron*. A sigmoid neuron is similar to a perceptron, but the presence of a sigmoid function rather than a binary filter now accepts any value between 0 and 1. This enables more flexibility to absorb small changes in edge weights without triggering inverse results—as the output is no longer binary. In other words, the output won't flip due to a minor change to an edge weight or input value.

While more flexible than a perceptron, a sigmoid neuron is unable to generate negative values. Hence, a third option is the *hyperbolic tangent function*.

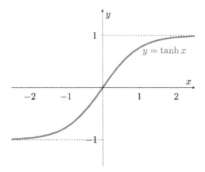

Figure 52: A hyperbolic tangent function graph

We have so far discussed basic neural networks; to develop a more advanced neural network, we can link sigmoid neurons and other classifiers to create a network with a higher number of layers or combine multiple perceptrons to form a multilayer perceptron.

Multilayer Perceptrons

The multilayer perceptron (MLP), as with other ANN techniques, is an algorithm for predicting a categorical (classification) or continuous (regression) target variable. Multilayer perceptrons are powerful because they aggregate multiple models into a unified prediction model, as demonstrated by the classification model shown in Figure 53.

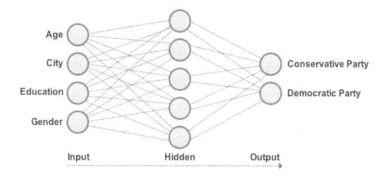

Figure 53: A multilayer perceptron used to classify a social media user's political preference

In this example, the MLP model is divided into three layers. The input layer consists of four nodes representing an input feature used to predict a social media user's political preference: Age, City, Education, and Gender. A function is then applied to each input variable to create a new layer of nodes called the middle or hidden layer. Each node in the hidden layer represents a function, such as a sigmoid function, but with its own unique weights/hyperparameters. This means that each input variable, in effect, is exposed to five different functions. Simultaneously, the hidden layer nodes are exposed to all four features.

The final output layer for this model consists of two discrete outcomes: Conservative Party or Democratic Party, which classifies the sample user's likely political preference. Note that the number of nodes at each layer will vary according to the number of input features and the target variable(s).

In general, multilayer perceptrons are ideal for interpreting large and complex datasets with no time or computational restraints. Less compute-intensive algorithms, such as decision trees and logistic regression, for example, are more efficient for working with smaller datasets. Given their high number of hyperparameters, multilayer perceptrons also demand more time and effort to tune than other algorithms. In regards to processing time, a multilayer perceptron takes longer to run than most shallow learning techniques including logistic regression but is generally faster than SVM.

Deep Learning

For analyzing less complex patterns, a basic multilayer perceptron or an alternative classification algorithm such as logistic regression and k-nearest neighbors can be put into practice. However, as patterns in the data become more complicated—especially in the form of a model with a high number of inputs such as image pixels—a shallow model is no longer reliable or capable of sophisticated analysis because the model becomes exponentially complicated as the number of inputs increases. A neural network, with a deep number of layers, though, can be used to interpret a high number of input features and break down complex patterns into simpler patterns, as shown in Figure 54.

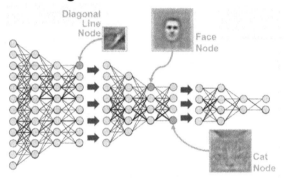

Figure 54: Facial recognition using deep learning. *Source: kdnuggets.com*

This deep neural network uses edges to detect different physical features to recognize faces, such as a diagonal line. Like building blocks, the network combines the node results to classify the input as, say, a human's face or a cat's face and then advances further to recognize individual characteristics. This is known as *deep learning*. What makes deep learning "deep" is the stacking of at least 5-10 node layers.

Object recognition, as used by self-driving cars to recognize objects such as pedestrians and other vehicles, uses upward of 150 layers and is a popular application of deep learning. Other applications of deep learning include time series analysis to analyze data trends measured over set time periods or intervals, speech recognition, and text processing tasks including sentiment analysis, topic segmentation, and named entity recognition. More usage scenarios and commonly paired deep learning techniques are listed in Table 13.

	Recurrent Network	Recursive Neural Tensor Network	Deep Belief Network	Convolution Network	MLP
Text Processing	✔	✔		✔	
Image Recognition			✔	✔	
Object Recognition		✔		✔	
Speech Recognition	✔				
Time Series Analysis	✔				
Classification			✔	✔	✔

Table 13: Common usage scenarios and paired deep learning techniques

As can be seen from this table, multilayer perceptrons (MLP) have largely been superseded by new deep learning techniques such as convolution networks, recurrent networks, deep belief networks, and recursive neural tensor networks (RNTN). These more advanced versions of a neural network can be used effectively across a number of practical applications that are in vogue today. While convolution networks are arguably the most popular and powerful of deep learning techniques, new methods and variations are continuously evolving.

CHAPTER QUIZ

Using a **multilayer perceptron**, your job is to create a model to classify the gender sex) of penguins that have been affected and rescued during a natural disaster. However, you can only use the physical attributes of penguins to train your model. Please note that this dataset has 344 rows.

	species	island	bill_length_mm	bill_depth_mm	flipper_length_mm	body_mass_g	sex
0	Adelie	Torgersen	39.1	18.7	181.0	3750.0	MALE
1	Adelie	Torgersen	39.5	17.4	186.0	3800.0	FEMALE
2	Adelie	Torgersen	40.3	18.0	195.0	3250.0	FEMALE
3	Adelie	Torgersen	NaN	NaN	NaN	NaN	NaN
4	Adelie	Torgersen	36.7	19.3	193.0	3450.0	FEMALE
5	Adelie	Torgersen	39.3	20.6	190.0	3650.0	MALE
6	Adelie	Torgersen	38.9	17.8	181.0	3625.0	FEMALE
7	Adelie	Torgersen	39.2	19.6	195.0	4675.0	MALE
8	Adelie	Torgersen	34.1	18.1	193.0	3475.0	NaN
9	Adelie	Torgersen	42.0	20.2	190.0	4250.0	NaN

1) **How many output nodes does the multilayer perceptron need to predict the dependent variable of sex (gender)?**

2) **Which of the seven variables could we use as independent variables**

based on only the penguin's physical attributes?

3) Which is a more transparent classification algorithm that we could use in replace of a multilayer perceptron?

A. Simple linear regression
B. Logistic regression
C. *k*-means clustering
D. Multiple linear regression

ANSWERS

1) 2 nodes (male and female)

2) bill_length_mm, bill_depth_mm, flipper_length_mm, body_mass_g

3) B, Logistic regression

DECISION TREES

The idea that artificial neural networks can be used to solve a wider spectrum of learning tasks than other techniques has led some pundits to hail ANN as the ultimate machine learning algorithm. While there is a strong case for this argument, this isn't to say that ANN fits the bill as a silver bullet algorithm. In certain cases, neural networks fall short, and decision trees are held up as a popular counterargument.

The huge amount of input data and computational resources required to train a neural network is the first downside of any attempt to solve all machine learning problems using this technique. Neural network-based applications like Google's image recognition engine rely on millions of tagged examples to recognize classes of simple objects (such as dogs) and not every organization has the resources available to feed and power a model of that size. The other major downside of neural networks is the black-box dilemma, which conceals the model's decision structure. Decision trees, on the other hand, are transparent and easy to interpret. They work with less data and consume less computational resources. These benefits make decision trees a popular alternative to deploying a neural network for less complex use cases.

Decision trees are used primarily for solving classification problems but can also be used as a regression model to predict numeric outcomes. Classification trees predict categorical outcomes using numeric and categorical variables as input, whereas regression trees predict numeric outcomes using numeric and categorical variables as input. Decision trees can be applied to a wide range of use cases; from picking a scholarship recipient, to predicting e-commerce sales, and selecting the right job applicant.

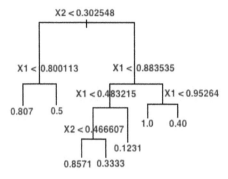

Figure 55: Example of a regression tree

Figure 56: Example of a classification tree

Part of the appeal of decision trees is they can be displayed graphically and they are easy to explain to non-experts. When a customer queries why they weren't selected for a home loan, for example, you can share the decision tree to show the decision-making process, which isn't possible using a black-box technique.

Building a Decision Tree

Decision trees start with a root node that acts as a starting point and is followed by splits that produce branches, also known as *edges*. The branches then link to leaves, also known as *nodes*, which form decision points. This process is repeated using the data points collected in each new leaf. A final categorization is produced when a leaf no longer generates any new branches and results in what's called a terminal node.

Beginning first at the root node, decision trees analyze data by splitting data into subsets, with a node for each value of the variable (i.e. sunny, overcast, rainy). The aim is to keep the tree as small as possible. This is achieved by selecting a variable that optimally splits the data into homogenous groups, such that it minimizes the level of data entropy at the next branch.

Entropy is a mathematical concept that explains the measure of variance in the data among different classes. In simple terms, we want the data at each layer to be more homogenous than the previous partition. We therefore want to pick a "greedy" algorithm that can reduce entropy at each layer of the tree. An example of a greedy algorithm is the Iterative Dichotomizer (ID3), invented by J.R. Quinlan. This is one of three decision tree implementations developed by Quinlan, hence the "3." At each layer, ID3 identifies a variable (converted into a binary question) that produces the least entropy at the next layer.

To understand how this works, let's consider the following example.

Employees	Exceeded KPIs	Leadership Capability	Aged < 30	Outcome
6	6	2	3	Promoted
4	0	2	4	Not promoted

Table 14: Employee characteristics

In this table we have ten employees, three input variables (Exceeded KPIs, Leadership Capability, Aged < 30), and one output variable (Outcome). Our aim is to classify whether an employee will be promoted/not promoted based on the assessment of the three input variables.

Let's first split the data by variable 1 (Exceeded Key Performance Indicators):

- Six promoted employees who exceeded their KPIs (Yes).

- Four employees who did not exceed their KPIs and who were not promoted (No).

This variable produces two homogenous groups at the next layer.

Exceeded KPIs?

Black = Promoted, White = Not Promoted

Now let's try variable 2 (Leadership Capability), which produces:

- Two promoted employees with leadership capabilities (Yes).

- Four promoted employees with no leadership capabilities (No).

- Two employees with leadership capabilities who were not promoted (Yes).

- Two employees with no leadership capabilities who were not promoted (No).

This variable produces two groups of mixed data points.

Leadership Capability?

Yes | No

Black = Promoted, White = Not Promoted

Lastly, we have variable 3 (Aged Under 30), which produces:

- Three promoted employees aged under thirty (Yes).
- Three promoted employees aged over thirty (No).
- Four employees aged under thirty who were not promoted (Yes).

This variable produces one homogenous group and one mixed group of data points.

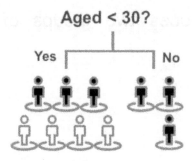

Aged < 30?

Yes | No

Black = Promoted, White = Not Promoted

Of these three variables, variable 1 (Exceeded KPIs) produces the best split with two perfectly homogenous groups. Variable 3 produces the second-best outcome, as one leaf is homogenous. Variable 2 produces two leaves that are heterogeneous. Variable 1 would therefore be selected as the first binary question to split this dataset.

Whether it's ID3 or another algorithm, this process of splitting data into sub-partitions, known as *recursive partitioning*, is repeated until a stopping criterion is met. A stopping point can be based on a range of criteria, such as:

- When all leaves contain less than 3-5 items.

- When a branch produces a result that places all items in one binary leaf.

Calculating Entropy

In this next section, we will review the mathematical calculations for finding the variables that produce the lowest entropy.

As mentioned, building a decision tree starts with setting a variable as the root node, with each outcome for that variable assigned a branch to a new decision node, i.e. "Yes" and "No." A second variable is then chosen to split the variables further to create new branches and decision nodes.

As we want the nodes to collect as many instances of the same class as possible, we need to select each variable strategically based on entropy, also called *information value*. Measured in units called bits (using a base 2 logarithm expression), entropy is calculated based on the composition of data points found in each node.

Using the following logarithm equation, we will calculate the entropy for each potential variable split expressed in bits between 0 and 1.

$$(-p_1 \log p_1 - p_2 \log p_2) / \log 2$$

Please note the logarithm equations can be quickly calculated online using Google Calculator.

Exceeded KPIs?

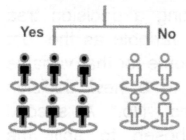

Yes: $p_1[6,6]$ and $p_2[0,6]$
No: $p_1[4,4]$ and $p_2[0,4]$

Step 1: Find entropy of each node
$(-p_1\log p_1 - p_2\log p_2) / \log 2$

Yes: $(-6/6*\log 6/6 - 0/6*\log 0/6) / \log 2 = 0$
No: $(-4/4*\log 4/4 - 0/4*\log 0/4) / \log 2 = 0$

Step 2: Multiply entropy of the two nodes in accordance to the total number of data points (10)

Leadership Capability?

Yes: $p_1[2,4]$ and $p_2[2,4]$

No: $p_1[4,6]$ and $p_2[2,6]$

Step 1: Find entropy of each node

Yes: $(-2/4*\log2/4 - 2/4*\log2/4) / \log2 = 1$

No: $(-4/6*\log4/6 - 2/6*\log2/6) / \log2 = 0.91829583405$

Step 2: Multiple entropy of the two nodes by total number of data points

$(4/10) \times 1 + (6/10) \times 0.918$

$0.4 + 0.5508 = 0.9508$

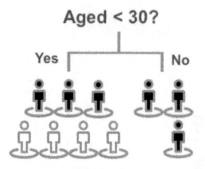

Aged < 30?

Yes: $p_1[3,7]$ and $p_2[4,7]$

No: $p_1[3,3]$ and $p_2[0,3]$

Step 1: Find entropy of each node
Yes: $(-3/7*\log 3/7 - 4/7*\log 4/7) / \log 2 =$
0.98522813603
No: $(-3/3*\log 3/3 - 0/3*\log 0/3) / \log 2 = 0$

Step 2: Multiple entropy of the two nodes by total number of data points
$(7/10) \times 0.985 + (3/10) \times 0$
$0.6895 + 0 = 0.6895$

Results
Exceeded KPIs = 0 bits
Leadership Capability = 0.9508 bits
Aged < 30 = 0.6895 bits

Based on our calculations, the variable **Exceeded KPIs** generates a perfect classification, which means we don't need to develop the tree any further after examining this variable. The next best candidate was the variable **Aged < 30** at 0.6895 bits. **Leadership Capability** had the highest entropy with 0.9508 bits, which equates to a high level of disorder and almost no information gain. In fact, we can calculate the entropy of the data prior to any potential split to question the need for analyzing this variable.

Promoted 6/10, Not Promoted 4/10
(-6/10*log6/10 - 4/10*log4/10) / log2 = 0.971
0.971 - 0.9508 = 0.0202

Thus, subtracting the original entropy of the dataset by the variable of **Leadership Capability** leads to a marginal 0.0202 bits in overall information gain.

Overfitting

A notable caveat of decision trees is their susceptibility to overfit the model to the training data. Based on the patterns extracted from the training data, a decision tree is precise at analyzing and decoding the first round of data. However, the same decision tree may then fail to classify the test data, as there could be rules that it's yet to encounter or because the training/test data split was not representative of the full dataset. Also, because decision trees are formed by repeatedly splitting data points into partitions, a slight change to how the data is split at the top or middle of the tree could dramatically alter the final prediction and produce a different tree altogether. The offender, in this case, is our greedy algorithm.

Starting with the first split of the data, the greedy algorithm picks a variable that best partitions the data into homogenous groups. Like a kid seated in front of a box of cupcakes, the greedy algorithm is oblivious to the future repercussions of its short-term actions. The variable used to first split the data does not guarantee the most accurate model at the end of production. Instead, a less effective split at the top of the tree might produce a more accurate model. Thus, although decision trees are highly visual and effective at classifying a single set of data, they are also inflexible and vulnerable to overfitting, especially for datasets with high pattern variance.

Bagging

Rather than aiming for the most efficient split at each round of recursive partitioning, an alternative technique is to construct multiple trees and combine their predictions. A popular example of this technique is *bagging,* which involves growing multiple decision trees using a randomized selection of input data for each tree and combining the results by averaging the output (for regression) or voting (for classification).

A key characteristic of bagging is *bootstrap sampling*. For multiple decision trees to generate unique insight, there needs to be an element of variation and randomness across each model. There's little sense in compiling five or ten identical models. Bootstrap sampling overcomes this problem by extracting a random variation of the data at each round, and in the case of bagging, different variations of the training data are run through each tree. While this doesn't eliminate the problem of overfitting, the dominant patterns in the dataset will appear in a higher number of trees and emerge in the final class or prediction. As a result, bagging is an effective algorithm for dealing with outliers and lowering the degree of variance typically found with a single decision tree.

Random Forests

A closely related technique to bagging is *random forests*. While both techniques grow multiple trees and utilize bootstrap sampling to randomize the data, random forests artificially limit the choice of variables by capping the number of variables considered for each split. In other words, the algorithm is not allowed to consider all n variables at each partition.

In the case of bagging, the trees often look similar because they use the same variable early in their decision structure in a bid to reduce entropy. This means the trees' predictions are highly correlated and closer to a single decision tree in regards to overall variance. Random forests sidestep this problem by forcing each split to consider a limited subset of variables, which gives other variables a greater chance of selection, and by averaging unique and uncorrelated trees, the final decision structure is less variable and often more reliable. As the model is trained using a subset of variables fewer than those actually available, random forests are considered a weakly-supervised learning technique.

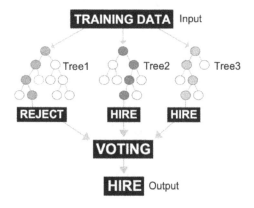

Figure 57: Example of growing random trees to produce a prediction

In general, random forests favor a high number of trees (i.e. 100+) to smooth out the potential impact of outliers, but there is a diminishing rate of effectiveness as more trees are added. At a certain level, new trees may not add any significant improvement to the model other than to extend the model's processing time. While it will depend on your dataset, 100-150 decision trees is a recommended starting point. Author and data expert Scott Hartshorn advises focusing on optimizing other hyperparameters before adding more trees to the initial model, as this will reduce processing time in the short-term and increasing the number of trees later should provide at least some added benefit.[24]

While random forests are versatile and work well at interpreting complex data patterns, other techniques including gradient boosting tend to return superior prediction accuracy. Random forests, though, are fast to train and work well for obtaining a quick benchmark model.

Boosting

Boosting is another family of algorithms that centers on aggregating a large pool of decision trees. The emphasis of boosting algorithms is on combining "weak" models into one "strong" model. The term "weak" means the initial model is a poor predictor and perhaps marginally better than a random guess. A "strong" model, meanwhile, is considered a reliable predictor of the true target output.

The concept of developing strong learners from weak learners is achieved by adding weights to trees based on misclassified cases in the previous tree. This is similar to a school teacher improving his or her class' performance by offering extra tutoring to students that performed badly on the most recent exam.

One of the more popular boosting algorithms is *gradient boosting*. Rather than selecting combinations of variables at random, gradient boosting selects variables that improve prediction accuracy with each new tree. The decision trees are therefore grown sequentially, as each tree is created using information derived from the previous tree, rather than independently.

Mistakes incurred in the training data are recorded and then applied to the next round of training data. At each iteration, weights are added to the training data based on the results of the previous iteration. A higher weighting is applied to instances that were incorrectly predicted from the training data, and instances that were correctly predicted receive less attention. Earlier iterations that don't perform well and that perhaps misclassified data can subsequently be improved upon in further iterations. This process is repeated until there's a low level of error. The final result is then obtained from a weighted average of the total predictions derived from each decision tree.

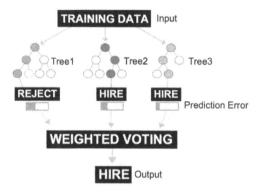

Figure 58: Example of reducing prediction error across multiple trees to produce a prediction

Boosting also mitigates the issue of overfitting and it does so using fewer trees than random forests. While adding more trees to a random forest usually helps to offset overfitting, the same process can cause overfitting in the case of boosting and caution should be taken as new trees are added.

The tendency of boosting algorithms towards overfitting can be explained by their highly-tuned focus of learning and reiterating from earlier mistakes. Although this typically translates to more accurate predictions—superior to that of most algorithms—it can lead to mixed results in the case of data stretched by a high number of outliers. In general, machine learning models should not fit too close to outlier cases, but this can be difficult for boosting algorithms to obey as they are constantly reacting to errors observed and isolated during production. For complex datasets with a large number of outliers, random forests may be a preferred alternative approach to boosting.

The other main downside of boosting is the slow processing speed that comes with training a sequential decision model. As trees are trained sequentially, each tree must wait for the previous tree, thereby limiting the production scalability of the model and especially as more trees are added. A random forest, meanwhile, is trained in parallel, making it faster to train.

The final downside, which applies to boosting as well as random forests and bagging, is the loss of visual simplicity and ease of interpretation that comes with using a single decision tree. When you have hundreds of decision trees it becomes more difficult to visualize and interpret the overall decision structure.

If, however, you have the time and resources to train a boosting model and a dataset with consistent patterns, the final model *can be* extremely worthwhile. Once deployed, predictions from the trained decision model can be generated quickly and accurately using this algorithm, and outside of deep learning, boosting is one of the most popular algorithms in machine learning today.

CHAPTER QUIZ

Your task is to predict the body mass (body_mass_g) of penguins using the penguin dataset and the **random forests** algorithm.

	species	bill_length_mm	bill_depth_mm	flipper_length_mm	body_mass_g	sex
0	Adelie	39.1	18.7	181.0	3750.0	MALE
1	Adelie	39.5	17.4	186.0	3800.0	FEMALE
2	Adelie	40.3	18.0	195.0	3250.0	FEMALE
3	Adelie	NaN	NaN	NaN	NaN	NaN
4	Adelie	36.7	19.3	193.0	3450.0	FEMALE
5	Adelie	39.3	20.6	190.0	3650.0	MALE
6	Adelie	38.9	17.8	181.0	3625.0	FEMALE
7	Adelie	39.2	19.6	195.0	4675.0	MALE
8	Adelie	34.1	18.1	193.0	3475.0	NaN
9	Adelie	42.0	20.2	190.0	4250.0	NaN

1) Which variables could we use as independent variables to train our model?

2) To train a quick benchmark model, gradient boosting is faster to train than random forests. True or False?

3) Which tree-based technique can be easily visualized?

A. Decision trees

B. Gradient boosting

C. Random forests

ANSWERS

1) All variables except for body_mass_g

(Tree-based techniques work well with both discrete and continuous variables as input variables.)

2) False

(Gradient boosting runs sequentially, making it slower to train. A random forest is trained simultaneously, making it faster to train.)

3) A, Decision trees

ENSEMBLE MODELING

When making important decisions, we generally prefer to collate multiple opinions as opposed to listening to a single perspective or the first person to voice their opinion. Similarly, it's important to consider and trial more than one algorithm to find the best model for your data. In advanced machine learning, it can even be advantageous to combine algorithms or models using a method called *ensemble modeling*, which amalgamates outputs to build a unified prediction model. By combining the output of different models (instead of relying on a single estimate), ensemble modeling helps to build a consensus on the meaning of the data. Aggregated estimates are also generally more accurate than any one technique. It's vital, though, for the ensemble models to display some degree of variation to avoid mishandling the same errors.

In the case of classification, multiple models are consolidated into a single prediction using a voting system[25] based on frequency, or numeric averaging in the case of regression problems.[26],[27] Ensemble models can also be divided into sequential or parallel and homogenous or heterogeneous.

Let's start by looking at sequential and parallel models. In the case of the former, the model's prediction error is reduced by adding weights to classifiers that previously misclassified data. Gradient boosting and AdaBoost (designed for classification problems) are both examples of sequential models. Conversely, parallel ensemble models work concurrently and reduce error by averaging. Random forests are an example of this technique.

Ensemble models can be generated using a single technique with numerous variations, known as a homogeneous ensemble, or through different techniques, known as a heterogeneous ensemble. An example of a homogeneous ensemble model would be multiple decision trees working together to form a single prediction (i.e. bagging). Meanwhile, an example of a heterogeneous ensemble would be the usage of *k*-means clustering or a neural network in collaboration with a decision tree algorithm.

Naturally, it's important to select techniques that complement each other. Neural networks, for instance, require complete data for analysis, whereas decision trees are competent at handling missing values.[28] Together, these two techniques provide added benefit over a homogeneous model. The neural network accurately predicts the majority of instances where a value is provided, and the decision tree ensures that there are no "null" results that would otherwise materialize from missing values using a neural network.

While the performance of an ensemble model outperforms a single algorithm in the majority of cases,[29] the degree of model complexity and sophistication can pose as a potential drawback. An ensemble model triggers the same trade-off in benefits as a single decision tree and a collection of trees, where the transparency and ease of interpretation of, say decision trees, is sacrificed for the accuracy of a more complex algorithm such as random forests, bagging or boosting. The performance of the model will win out in most cases, but interpretability is an important factor to consider when choosing the right algorithm(s) for your data.

In terms of selecting a suitable ensemble modeling technique, there are four main methods: bagging, boosting, a bucket of models, and stacking.

As a heterogeneous ensemble technique, a **bucket of models** trains multiple different algorithmic models using the same training data and then picks the one that performed most accurately on the test data.

Bagging, as we know, is an example of parallel model averaging using a homogenous ensemble, which draws upon randomly drawn data and combines predictions to design a unified model.

Boosting is a popular alternative technique that is still a homogenous ensemble but addresses error and data misclassified by the previous iteration to produce a sequential model. Gradient boosting and AdaBoost are both examples of boosting algorithms.

Stacking runs multiple models simultaneously on the data and combines those results to produce a final model. Unlike boosting and bagging, stacking usually combines outputs from different algorithms (heterogenous) rather than altering the hyperparameters of the same algorithm (homogenous). Also, rather than assigning equal trust to each model using averaging or voting, stacking attempts to identify and add emphasis to well-performing models. This is achieved by smoothing out the error rate of models at the base level (known as level-0) using a weighting system, before pushing those outputs to the level-1 model where they are combined and consolidated into a final prediction.

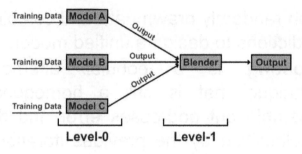

Figure 59: Stacking algorithm

While this technique is sometimes used in industry, the gains of using a stacking technique are marginal in line with the level of the complexity, and organizations usually opt for the ease and efficiency of boosting or bagging. Stacking, though, is a go-to technique for machine learning competitions like the Kaggle Challenges and the Netflix Prize. The Netflix competition, held between 2006 and 2009, offered a prize for a machine learning model that could significantly improve Netflix's content recommender system. One of the winning techniques, from the team *BellKor's Pragmatic Chaos*, adopted a form of linear stacking that blended predictions from hundreds of different models using different algorithms.

DEVELOPMENT ENVIRONMENT

After examining the statistical underpinnings of numerous algorithms, it's time to turn our attention to the coding component of machine learning and installing a development environment.

Although there are various options in regards to programming languages (as outlined in Chapter 4), Python has been chosen for this three-part exercise as it's easy to learn and widely used in industry and online learning courses. If you don't have any experience in programming or coding with Python, there's no need to worry. Feel free to skip the code and focus on the text explanations to understand the steps involved. A primer on programming with Python is also included in the Appendix section of this book.

As for our development environment, we will be installing Jupyter Notebook, which is an open-source web application that allows for the editing and sharing of code notebooks. Jupyter Notebook can be installed using the Anaconda Distribution or Python's package manager, pip. As an experienced Python user, you may wish to install Jupyter Notebook via pip, and there are instructions available on the Jupyter Notebook website (http://jupyter.org/install.html) outlining this option. For beginners, I recommend choosing the Anaconda Distribution option, which offers an easy click-and-drag setup (https://www.anaconda.com/products/individual/).

This installation option will direct you to the Anaconda website. From there, you can select an Anaconda installer for Windows, macOS, or Linux. Again, you can find instructions available on the Anaconda website as per your choice of operating system.

After installing Anaconda to your machine, you'll have access to a range of data science applications including rstudio, Jupyter Notebook, and graphviz for data visualization. For this exercise, select Jupyter Notebook by clicking on "Launch" inside the Jupyter Notebook tab.

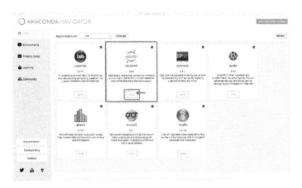

Figure 60: The Anaconda Navigator portal

To initiate Jupyter Notebook, run the following command from the Terminal (for Mac/Linux) or Command Prompt (for Windows):

jupyter notebook

Terminal/Command Prompt then generates a URL for you to copy and paste into your web browser. Example: http://localhost:8888/
Copy and paste the generated URL into your web browser to load Jupyter

Notebook. Once you have Jupyter Notebook open in your browser, click on "New" in the top right-hand corner of the web application to create a new notebook project, and then select "Python 3." You're now ready to begin coding. Next, we'll explore the basics of working in Jupyter Notebook.

Figure 61: Screenshot of a new notebook

Import Libraries

The first step of any machine learning project in Python is installing the necessary code libraries. These libraries will differ from project to project based on the composition of your data and what you wish to achieve, i.e., data visualization, ensemble modeling, deep learning, etc.

```
In [1]:   1  # Import library
          2  import pandas as pd
          3
```

Figure 62: Import Pandas

In the code snippet above is the example code to import Pandas, which is a popular Python library used in machine learning.

Import Dataset and Preview

We can now use Pandas to import our dataset. I've selected a free and publicly available dataset from kaggle.com which contains data on house, unit, and townhouse prices in Melbourne, Australia. This dataset comprises data scraped from publicly available listings posted weekly on www.domain.com.au. The full dataset contains 34,857 property listings and 21 variables including address, suburb, land size, number of rooms, price, longitude, latitude, postcode, etc.

The Melbourne_housing_FULL dataset can be downloaded from this link: https://www.kaggle.com/anthonypino/melbourne-housing-market/.

After registering a free account and logging into kaggle.com, download the dataset as a zip file. Next, unzip the downloaded file and import it into Jupyter Notebook. To import the dataset, you can use pd.read_csv to load the data into a Pandas dataframe (tabular dataset).

```
df =
pd.read_csv('~/Downloads/Melbourne_housing_FULL.c
sv')
```

This command directly imports the dataset into Jupyter Notebook. However, please note that the file path depends on the saved location of your dataset and your computer's operating system. For example, if you saved the CSV file to your (Mac) desktop, you would need to import the .csv file using the following command:

```
df =
pd.read_csv('~/Desktop/Melbourne_housing_FULL.csv'
)
```

In my case, I imported the dataset from my Downloads folder. As you move forward in machine learning and data science, it's important that you save datasets and projects in standalone and named folders for organized access. If you opt to save the .csv in the same folder as your Jupyter Notebook, you won't need to append a directory name or ~/ .

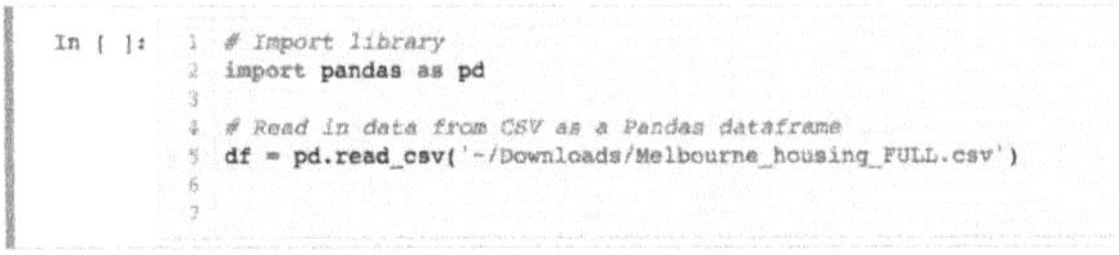

```
In [ ]:   1  # Import library
          2  import pandas as pd
          3
          4  # Read in data from CSV as a Pandas dataframe
          5  df = pd.read_csv('~/Downloads/Melbourne_housing_FULL.csv')
          6
          7
```

Figure 63: Import dataset as a dataframe

If saved to Desktop on Windows, you would import the .csv file using a structure similar to this example:

df = pd.read_csv('C:\\Users\\John\\Desktop\\Melbourne_hou sing_FULL.csv')

Next, use the head() command to preview the dataframe.

df.head()

Right-click and select "Run" or navigate from the Jupyter Notebook menu: Cell > Run All

Figure 64: "Run All" from the navigation menu

This populates the dataset as a Pandas dataframe within Jupyter Notebook as shown in Figure 65.

Figure 65: Previewing a dataframe in Jupyter Notebook

The default number of rows displayed using the head() command is five. To set an alternative number of rows to display, enter the desired number directly inside the parentheses as shown below in Figure 66.

df.head(10)

```
In [2]:  # Import library
         import pandas as pd

         # Read in data from CSV as a Pandas dataframe
         df = pd.read_csv('~/Downloads/Melbourne_housing_FULL.csv')

         df.head(10)
Out[2]:
```

	Suburb	Address	Rooms	Type	Price	Method	SellerG	Date	Distance	Postcode	...	Bathroom	Car	Landsize
0	Abbotsford	68 Studley St	2	h	NaN	SS	Jellis	3/09/2016	2.5	3067.0	...	1.0	1.0	126.0
1	Abbotsford	85 Turner St	2	h	1480000.0	S	Biggin	3/12/2016	2.5	3067.0	...	1.0	1.0	202.0
2	Abbotsford	25 Bloomburg St	2	h	1035000.0	S	Biggin	4/02/2016	2.5	3067.0	...	1.0	0.0	156.0
3	Abbotsford	18/659 Victoria St	3	u	NaN	VB	Rounds	4/02/2016	2.5	3067.0	...	2.0	1.0	0.0
4	Abbotsford	5 Charles St	3	h	1465000.0	SP	Biggin	4/03/2017	2.5	3067.0	...	2.0	0.0	134.0
5	Abbotsford	40 Federation La	3	h	850000.0	PI	Biggin	4/03/2017	2.5	3067.0	...	2.0	1.0	94.0
6	Abbotsford	55a Park St	4	h	1600000.0	VB	Nelson	4/06/2016	2.5	3067.0	...	1.0	2.0	120.0
7	Abbotsford	16 Maugie St	4	h	NaN	SN	Nelson	6/08/2016	2.5	3067.0	...	2.0	2.0	400.0
8	Abbotsford	53 Turner St	2	h	NaN	S	Biggin	6/08/2016	2.5	3067.0	...	1.0	2.0	201.0
9	Abbotsford	99 Turner St	2	h	NaN	S	Collins	6/08/2016	2.5	3067.0	...	2.0	1.0	202.0

10 rows × 21 columns

Figure 66: Previewing a dataframe with 10 rows

This now previews a dataframe with ten rows. You'll also notice that the total number of rows and columns (10 rows x 21 columns) is listed below the dataframe on the left-hand side.

Find Row Item

While the head command is useful for gaining a general idea of the shape of your dataframe, it's difficult to find specific information from datasets with hundreds or thousands of rows. In machine learning, you often need to locate a specific row by matching a row number with its row information. For example, if our machine learning model finds that row 100 is the most suitable house to recommend to a potential buyer, we next need to see which house that is in the dataframe.

This can be achieved by using the iloc[] command as shown here:

```
In [3]:  1  # Import library
         2  import pandas as pd
         3
         4  # Read in data from CSV as a Pandas dataframe
         5  df = pd.read_csv('~/Downloads/Melbourne_housing_FULL.csv')
         6
         7  df.iloc[100]
         8

Out[3]:  Suburb                              Airport West
         Address                            180 Parer Rd
         Rooms                                         3
         Type                                          h
         Price                                    830000
         Method                                        S
         SellerG                                   Barry
         Date                                 16/04/2016
         Distance                                   13.5
         Postcode                                   3042
         Bedroom2                                      3
         Bathroom                                      1
         Car                                           2
         Landsize                                    971
         BuildingArea                                113
         YearBuilt                                  1960
         CouncilArea         Moonee Valley City Council
         Lattitude                              -37.7186
         Longtitude                              144.876
         Regionname              Western Metropolitan
         Propertycount                              3464
         Name: 100, dtype: object
```

Figure 67: Finding a row using .iloc[ ]

In this example, df.iloc[100] is used to find the row indexed at position 100 in the dataframe, which is a property located in Airport West. Be careful to note that the first row in a Python dataframe is indexed as 0. Thus, the Airport West property is technically the 101st property contained in the dataframe.

Print Columns

The final code snippet I'd like to introduce to you is columns , which is a convenient method to print the dataset's column titles. This will prove useful later when configuring which features to select, modify or remove from the model.

df.columns

```
In [4]:  1  # Import library
         2  import pandas as pd
         3
         4  # Read in data from CSV as a Pandas dataframe
         5  df = pd.read_csv('~/Downloads/Melbourne_housing_FULL.csv')
         6
         7  df.columns
         8

Out[4]:  Index(['Suburb', 'Address', 'Rooms', 'Type', 'Price', 'Method', 'SellerG',
                'Date', 'Distance', 'Postcode', 'Bedroom2', 'Bathroom', 'Car',
                'Landsize', 'BuildingArea', 'YearBuilt', 'CouncilArea', 'Lattitude',
                'Longtitude', 'Regionname', 'Propertycount'],
               dtype='object')
```

Figure 68: Print columns

Again, "Run" the code to view the outcome, which in this case is the 21 column titles and their data type (dtype), which is 'object.' You may notice that some of the column titles are misspelled. We'll discuss this issue in the next chapter.

BUILDING A MODEL IN PYTHON

We're now ready to design a full machine learning model building on the code introduced in the previous chapter.

For this exercise, we will design a house price valuation system using gradient boosting following these six steps:

1) Import libraries
2) Import dataset
3) Scrub dataset
4) Split data into training and test data
5) Select an algorithm and configure its hyperparameters
6) Evaluate the results

1) Import Libraries

To build our model, we first need to import Pandas and a number of functions from Scikit-learn, including gradient boosting (ensemble) and mean absolute error to evaluate performance.

Import each of the following libraries by entering these exact commands in Jupyter Notebook:

```
#Import libraries
import pandas as pd
from sklearn.model_selection import train_test_split
from sklearn import ensemble
from sklearn.metrics import mean_absolute_error
```

Don't worry if you don't recognize each of the Scikit-learn libraries displayed in the code snippet above as they will be referred to in later steps.

2) Import Dataset

Use the pd.read_csv command to load the Melbourne Housing Market dataset (as we did in the previous chapter) into a Pandas dataframe.

```
df = pd.read_csv('~/Downloads/Melbourne_housing_FULL.csv')
```

Please also note that the property values in this dataset are expressed in

Australian Dollars—$1 AUD is
approximately $0.77 USD (as of 2017).

Feature	Data Type	Continuous/Discrete
Suburb	String	Discrete
Address	String	Discrete
Rooms	Integer	Continuous
Type	String	Discrete
Price	Integer	Continuous
Method	String	Discrete
SellerG (seller's name)	String	Discrete
Date	TimeDate	Discrete
Distance	Floating-point	Continuous
Postcode	Integer	Discrete
Bedroom2	Integer	Continuous
Bathroom	Integer	Continuous
Car	Integer	Continuous
Landsize	Integer	Continuous
BuildingArea	Integer	Continuous
YearBuilt	TimeDate	Discrete
CouncilArea	String	Discrete
Lattitude	String	Discrete
Longtitude	String	Discrete
Regionname	String	Discrete
Propertycount (in that suburb)	Integer	Continuous

Table 15: Melbourne housing dataset
variables

3) Scrub Dataset

This next stage involves scrubbing the
dataset. Remember, scrubbing is the
process of refining your dataset such as
modifying or removing incomplete,
irrelevant or duplicated data. It may also
entail converting text-based data to
numeric values and the redesigning of
features.

It's worthwhile to note that some aspects
of data scrubbing may take place prior to

importing the dataset into the development environment. For instance, the creator of the Melbourne Housing Market dataset misspelled "Longitude" and "Latitude" in the head columns. As we will not be examining these two variables in our model, there's no need to make any changes. If, however, we did choose to include these two variables in our model, it would be prudent to amend this error in the source file.

From a programming perspective, spelling mistakes contained in the column titles don't pose a problem as long as we apply the same spelling to perform our code commands. However, this misnaming of columns could lead to human errors, especially if you are sharing your code with other team members. To avoid confusion, it's best to fix spelling mistakes and other simple errors in the source file before importing the dataset into Jupyter Notebook or another development environment. You can do this by opening the CSV file in Microsoft Excel (or equivalent program), editing the dataset, and then resaving it again as a CSV file.

While simple errors can be corrected in the source file, major structural changes to the dataset such as removing variables or missing values are best performed in the development environment for added flexibility and to preserve the original dataset for future use. Manipulating the composition of the dataset in the development environment is less permanent and is generally easier and quicker to implement than doing so in the source file.

Scrubbing Process

Let's remove columns we don't wish to include in the model using the delete command and entering the vector (column) titles we wish to remove.

```
# The misspellings of "longitude" and "latitude" are
preserved here
del df['Address']
del df['Method']
del df['SellerG']
del df['Date']
del df['Postcode']
del df['Lattitude']
del df['Longtitude']
```

```
del df['Regionname']
del df['Propertycount']
```

The Address, Regionname, Postcode, Latitude, and Longitude columns were removed as property location is contained in other columns (Suburb and CouncilArea). My assumption is that Suburb and CouncilArea have more sway in buyers' minds than Postcode, Latitude, and Longitude—although Address deserves an honorable mention.

Method, SellerG, Propertycount, and Date were also removed because they were deemed to have less relevance in comparison to other variables. This is not to say that these variables don't impact property prices; rather the other eleven independent variables are sufficient for building our initial model. We can decide to add any one of these variables into the model later, and you may choose to include them in your own model.

The remaining eleven independent variables from the dataset are Suburb, Rooms, Type, Distance, Bedroom2, Bathroom, Car, Landsize, BuildingArea, YearBuilt, and CouncilArea. The twelfth variable is the dependent variable which is Price. As mentioned, decision tree-based models (including gradient boosting and random forests) are adept at managing large and high-dimensional datasets with a high number of input variables.

The next step for scrubbing the dataset is to remove missing values. While there's a number of methods to manage missing values (e.g., populating empty cells with the dataset's mean value, median value or deleting missing values altogether), for this exercise, we want to keep the dataset as simple as possible, and we'll not be examining rows with missing values. The obvious downside is that we have a reduced amount of data to analyze.

As a beginner, it makes sense to master complete datasets before adding an extra dimension of complexity in attempting to deal with missing values. Unfortunately, in the case of our sample dataset, we *do* have a lot of missing values! Nonetheless, there are still ample rows available to proceed with building our model after removing those that contain missing values.

The following Pandas command can be used to remove rows with missing values. For more information about the dropna method and its parameters, please see Table 16 or the Pandas documentation. [30]

df.dropna(axis = 0, how = 'any', thresh = None, subset = None, inplace = True)

Parameter	Argument	Explanation	Default
axis	0	Drops rows with missing values	✓
	1	Drops columns with missing values	
how	any	Drops rows or columns with any missing values	✓
	all	Drops rows or columns with all values missing	
thresh	integer	Set an integer threshold to activate column/row removal, i.e. "4" to remove rows or columns with 4 or more missing values.	
	None	Select "None" if you do not wish to set a threshold.	
subset	variable	Define which columns to search for missing values, i.e. 'genre'	
	None	Select "None" if you do not wish to set a subset.	
inplace	True	If True, do operation inplace (update rather than replace)	
	False		✓

Table 16: Dropna parameters

Keep in mind too that it's important to drop rows with missing values after applying the delete command to remove columns (as shown in the previous step). This way, there's a better chance of preserving more rows from the original dataset. Imagine dropping a whole row because it was missing the value for a variable that would later be deleted such as a missing post code!

Next, let's convert columns that contain non-numeric data to numeric values using one-hot encoding. With Pandas, one-hot encoding can be performed using the pd.get_dummies method.

```
df = pd.get_dummies(df, columns = ['Suburb',
'CouncilArea', 'Type'])
```

This code command converts column values for Suburb, CouncilArea, and Type into numeric values through the application of one-hot encoding.

Lastly, assign the dependent and independent variables with Price as y and X as the remaining 11 variables (with Price dropped from the dataframe using the drop method).

```
X = df.drop('Price',axis=1)
y = df['Price']
```

4) Split the Dataset

We are now at the stage of splitting the data into training and test segments. For this exercise, we'll proceed with a standard 70/30 split by calling the Scikit-learn command below with a test_size of "0.3" and shuffling the dataset.

```
X_train, X_test, y_train, y_test = train_test_split(X, y,
test_size = 0.3, shuffle = True)
```

5) Select Algorithm and Configure Hyperparameters

Next we need to assign our chosen algorithm (gradient boosting regressor) as a new variable (model) and configure its hyperparameters as demonstrated below.

```
model = ensemble.GradientBoostingRegressor(
    n_estimators = 150,
    learning_rate = 0.1,
    max_depth = 30,
    min_samples_split = 4,
    min_samples_leaf = 6,
    max_features = 0.6,
    loss = 'huber'
)
```

The first line is the algorithm itself (gradient boosting) and comprises just one line of code. The code below dictates the hyperparameters that accompany this algorithm.

n_estimators states the number of decision trees. Recall that a high number of trees generally improves accuracy (up to a certain point) but will inevitably extend the model's processing time. I have selected 150 decision trees as an initial starting point.

learning_rate controls the rate at which additional decision trees influence the overall prediction. This effectively shrinks the contribution of each tree by the set learning_rate . Inserting a low rate here, such as 0.1, should help to improve accuracy.

max_depth defines the maximum number of layers (depth) for each decision tree. If "None" is selected, then nodes expand until all leaves are pure or until all leaves contain less than min_samples_leaf . Here, I have chosen a high maximum number of layers (30), which will have a dramatic effect on the final output, as we'll soon see.

min_samples_split defines the minimum number of samples required to execute a new binary split. For example, min_samples_split = 10 means there must be ten available samples in order to create a new branch.

min_samples_leaf represents the minimum number of samples that must appear in each child node (leaf) before a new branch can be implemented. This helps to mitigate the impact of outliers and anomalies in the form of a low number of samples found in one leaf as a result of a binary split. For example, min_samples_leaf = 4 requires there to be at least four available samples within each leaf for a new branch to be created.

max_features is the total number of features presented to the model when determining the best split. As mentioned in Chapter 14, random forests and gradient boosting restrict the number of features fed to each individual tree to create multiple results that can be voted upon later.

If an integer (whole number), the model will consider max_features at each split (branch). If the value is a float (e.g., 0.6), then max_features is the percentage of total features randomly selected. Although it sets a maximum number of features to consider in identifying the best split, total features may exceed the set limit if no split can initially be made.

loss calculates the model's error rate. For this exercise, we are using huber which protects against outliers and anomalies. Alternative error rate options include ls (least squares regression), lad (least absolute deviations), and quantile (quantile regression). Huber is actually a combination of least squares regression and least absolute deviations.

To learn more about gradient boosting hyperparameters, please refer to the Scikit-learn documentation for this algorithm.[31]

After setting the model's hyperparameters, we'll use the fit() function from Scikit-learn to link the training data to the learning algorithm stored in the variable model to train the prediction model.

```
model.fit(X_train, y_train)
```

6) Evaluate the Results

After the model has been trained, we can use the predict() function from Scikit-learn to run the model on the X_train data and evaluate its performance against the actual y_train data. As mentioned earlier, for this exercise we are using mean absolute error to evaluate the accuracy of the model.

```
mae_train = mean_absolute_error(y_train,
model.predict(X_train))
print ("Training Set Mean Absolute Error: %.2f" %
mae_train)
```

Here, we input our y_train values, which represent the correct results from the training dataset. The predict() function is called on the X_train set and generates predictions. The mean_absolute_error function then compares the difference between the actual values and the model's predictions. The second line of the code then prints the results to two decimal places alongside the string (text) "Training Set Mean Absolute Error: ". The same process is also repeated using the test data.

```
mae_test = mean_absolute_error(y_test,
model.predict(X_test))
```

```
print ("Test Set Mean Absolute Error: %.2f" %
mae_test)
```

Let's now run the entire model by right-clicking and selecting "Run" or navigating from the Jupyter Notebook menu: Cell > Run All.

Wait 30 seconds or longer for the computer to process the training model. The results, as shown below, will then appear at the bottom of the notebook.

Training Set Mean Absolute Error: 27834.12

Test Set Mean Absolute Error: 168262.14

For this model, our training set's mean absolute error is $27,834.12, and the test set's mean absolute error is $168,262.14. This means that on average, the training set miscalculated the actual property value by $27,834.12. The test set, meanwhile, miscalculated the property value by $168,262.14 on average.

This means that our training model was accurate at predicting the actual value of properties contained in the training data. While $27,834.12 may seem like a lot of money, this average error value is low given the maximum range of our dataset is $8 million. As many of the properties in the dataset are in excess of seven figures ($1,000,000+), $27,834.12 constitutes a reasonably low error rate.

How did the model fare with the test data? The test data provided less accurate predictions with an average error rate of $168,262.14. A high discrepancy between the training and test data is usually an indicator of overfitting in the model. As our model is tailored to patterns in the training data, it stumbled when making predictions using the test data, which probably contains new patterns that the model hasn't seen. The test data, of course, is likely to carry slightly different patterns and new potential outliers and anomalies.

However, in this case, the difference between the training and test data is exacerbated because we configured our model to overfit the training data. An example of this issue was setting max_depth to "30." Although placing a high maximum depth improves the chances of the model finding patterns in the training data, it does tend to lead to overfitting.

Lastly, please take into account that because the training and test data are shuffled randomly, and data is fed to decision trees at random, the predicted results will differ slightly when replicating this model on your own machine.

A video version of this chapter is available as a mini course at https://scatterplotpress.com/p/house-prediction-model. The mini course is free and lets you follow along step-by-step through the workflow described in this chapter.

MODEL OPTIMIZATION

In the previous chapter we built our first supervised learning model. We now want to improve its prediction accuracy with future data and reduce the effects of overfitting. A good starting point is to modify the model's hyperparameters. Holding the other hyperparameters constant, let's begin by adjusting the maximum depth from "30" to "5." The model now generates the following results:

Training Set Mean Absolute Error: 135283.69

Although the mean absolute error of the training set is now higher, this helps to reduce the issue of overfitting and should improve the model's performance. Another step to optimize the model is to add more trees. If we set n_estimators to

250, we now see these results from the model:

Training Set Mean Absolute Error: 124469.48
Test Set Mean Absolute Error: 161602.45

This second optimization reduces the training set's absolute error rate by approximately $11,000 and there is a smaller gap between the training and test results for mean absolute error.[32]

Together, these two optimizations underline the importance of understanding the impact of individual hyperparameters. If you decide to replicate this supervised machine learning model at home, I recommend that you test modifying each of the hyperparameters individually and analyze their impact on mean absolute error using the training data. In addition, you'll notice changes in the machine's processing time based on the chosen hyperparameters. Changing the maximum number of branch layers (max_depth), for example, from "30" to "5" will dramatically reduce total processing time. Processing speed and resources will become an important consideration when you move on to working with larger datasets.

Another important optimization technique is feature selection. Earlier, we removed nine features from the dataset but now might be a good time to reconsider those features and test whether they have an impact on the model's prediction accuracy. "SellerG" would be an interesting feature to add to the model because the real estate company selling the property might have some impact on the final selling price.

Alternatively, dropping features from the current model may reduce processing time without having a significant impact on accuracy—or may even improve accuracy. When selecting features, it's best to isolate feature modifications and analyze the results, rather than applying various changes at once.

While manual trial and error can be a useful technique to understand the impact of variable selection and hyperparameters, there are also automated techniques for model optimization, such as *grid search*. Grid search allows you to list a range of configurations you wish to test for each hyperparameter and methodically test each of those possible hyperparameters. An automated voting process then takes place to determine the optimal model. As the model must examine each possible combination of hyperparameters, grid search does take a long time to run![33] It sometimes helps to run a relatively coarse grid search using consecutive powers of 10 (i.e. 0.01, 0.1, 1, 10) and then run a finer grid search around the best value identified.[34] Example code for grid search using Scikit-learn is included at the end of this chapter.

Another way of optimizing algorithm hyperparameters is the randomized search method using Scikit-learn's RandomizedSearchCV. This method trials far more hyperparameters per round than grid search (which only changes one single hyperparameter per round) as it uses a random value for each hyperparameter at each round. Randomized search also makes it simple to specify the number of trial rounds and control computing resources. Grid search, meanwhile, runs based on the full number of hyperparameter combinations, which isn't obvious from looking at the code and might take more time than expected.

Finally, if you wish to use a different supervised machine learning algorithm and not gradient boosting, the majority of the code used in this exercise can be reused. For instance, the same code can be used to import a new dataset, preview the dataframe, remove features (columns), remove rows, split and shuffle the dataset, and evaluate mean absolute error. The official website http://scikit-learn.org is also a great resource to learn more about other algorithms as well as gradient boosting used in this exercise.

To learn how to input and test an individual house valuation using the model we have built in these two chapters, please see this more advanced tutorial available at https://scatterplotpress.com/p/house-prediction-model.

. In addition, if you have trouble implementing the model using the code found in this book, please contact the author by email for assistance (oliver.theobald@scatterplotpress.com).

Code for the Optimized Model

```python
# Import libraries
import pandas as pd
from sklearn.model_selection import train_test_split
from sklearn import ensemble
from sklearn.metrics import mean_absolute_error

# Read in data from CSV
df =
pd.read_csv('~/Downloads/Melbourne_housing_FULL.c
sv')

# Delete unneeded columns
del df['Address']
del df['Method']
del df['SellerG']
del df['Date']
del df['Postcode']
del df['Lattitude']
del df['Longtitude']
del df['Regionname']
del df['Propertycount']

# Remove rows with missing values
df.dropna(axis = 0, how = 'any', thresh = None, subset
= None, inplace = True)

# Convert non-numeric data using one-hot encoding
df = pd.get_dummies(df, columns = ['Suburb',
'CouncilArea', 'Type'])

# Assign X and y variables
X = df.drop('Price',axis=1)
y = df['Price']
```

```python
# Split data into test/train set (70/30 split) and shuffle
X_train, X_test, y_train, y_test = train_test_split(X, y,
test_size = 0.3, shuffle = True)

# Set up algorithm
model = ensemble.GradientBoostingRegressor(
    n_estimators = 250,
    learning_rate = 0.1,
    max_depth = 5,
    min_samples_split = 4,
    min_samples_leaf = 6,
    max_features = 0.6,
    loss = 'huber'
)

# Run model on training data
model.fit(X_train, y_train)

# Check model accuracy (up to two decimal places)
mae_train = mean_absolute_error(y_train,
model.predict(X_train))
print ("Training Set Mean Absolute Error: %.2f" %
mae_train)

mae_test = mean_absolute_error(y_test,
model.predict(X_test))
print ("Test Set Mean Absolute Error: %.2f" %
mae_test)
```

Code for Grid Search Model

```python
# Import libraries, including GridSearchCV
import pandas as pd
from sklearn.model_selection import train_test_split
from sklearn import ensemble
from sklearn.metrics import mean_absolute_error
from sklearn.model_selection import GridSearchCV

# Read in data from CSV
df =
pd.read_csv('~/Downloads/Melbourne_housing_FULL.c
sv')

# Delete unneeded columns
del df['Address']
del df['Method']
del df['SellerG']
del df['Date']
del df['Postcode']
del df['Lattitude']
del df['Longtitude']

del df['Regionname']
del df['Propertycount']

# Remove rows with missing values
df.dropna(axis = 0, how = 'any', thresh = None, subset
= None, inplace = True)

# Convert non-numeric data using one-hot encoding
df = pd.get_dummies(df, columns = ['Suburb',
'CouncilArea', 'Type'])

# Assign X and y variables
X = df.drop('Price',axis=1)
y = df['Price']
```

```python
# Split data into test/train set (70/30 split) and shuffle
X_train, X_test, y_train, y_test = train_test_split(X, y,
test_size = 0.3, shuffle = True)

# Input algorithm
model = ensemble.GradientBoostingRegressor()

# Set the configurations that you wish to test. To
minimize processing time, limit num. of variables or
experiment on each hyperparameter separately.
hyperparameters = {
    'n_estimators': [200, 300],
    'max_depth': [4, 6],
    'min_samples_split': [3, 4],
    'min_samples_leaf': [5, 6],
    'learning_rate': [0.01, 0.02],
    'max_features': [0.8, 0.9],
    'loss': ['ls', 'lad', 'huber']
}

# Define grid search. Run with four CPUs in parallel if
applicable.
grid = GridSearchCV(model, hyperparameters, n_jobs
= 4)

# Run grid search on training data
grid.fit(X_train, y_train)
```

```python
# Return optimal hyperparameters
grid.best_params_

# Check model accuracy using optimal
hyperparameters
mae_train = mean_absolute_error(y_train,
grid.predict(X_train))
print ("Training Set Mean Absolute Error: %.2f" %
mae_train)

mae_test = mean_absolute_error(y_test,
grid.predict(X_test))
print ("Test Set Mean Absolute Error: %.2f" %
mae_test)
```

APPENDIX: INTRODUCTION TO PYTHON

Python was designed by Guido van Rossum at the National Research Institute for Mathematics and Computer Science in the Netherlands during the late 1980s and early 1990s. Derived from the Unix shell command-line interpreter and other programming languages including C and C++, it was designed to empower developers to write programs with fewer lines of code than other languages.[35] Unlike other programming languages, Python also incorporates many English keywords where other languages use punctuation.

In Python, the input code is read by the Python interpreter to perform an output. Any errors, including poor formatting, misspelled functions or random characters left someplace in your script are picked up by the Python interpreter and cause a syntax error.

In this appendix section, we will discuss basic syntax and concepts to help you write fluid and effective code using Python 3.

Comments

Adding comments is good practice in computer programming to signpost the purpose and content of your code. In Python, comments can be added to your code using the # (hash) character. Everything placed after the hash character (on that line of code) is then ignored by the Python interpreter.

Example:
```
# Import Melbourne Housing dataset from my Downloads folder
dataframe = pd.read_csv('~/Downloads/Melbourne_housing_FULL.csv')
```
In this example, the second line of code will be executed, while the first line of code will be ignored by the Python interpreter.

Python Data Types

Common data types in Python are shown in the following table.

Name	Explanation	Key Feature	Example
Integer	Whole numbers	No decimal point	50
Floating point	Numbers with a decimal placing	Decimal point	50.0
String	Words and characters	Single/double quote marks	"Fifty5" or 'Fifty5'
Lists	Ordered sequence of objects	Square brackets	[1,2,3,4,'machine learning']
Tuples	An ordered and immutable sequence of objects. Almost the same as a List, except values cannot be manipulated, thereby guaranteeing data integrity by preventing accidental changes in complex pieces of code.	Brackets	(1, 2 ,3 , 4)
Dictionaries	Key-value pair. The key is denoted by a string such as a file name and linked to a value such as an image or text.	Curly brackets, semi-colon, and quote marks	{"name": "john", "gender": "male"}
Sets	An unordered collection of unique objects	Curly brackets	{"1","2","a"}
Boolean	Binary value	Capital initial (T/F)	True or False

Table 17: Common Python data types

In machine learning, you will commonly be working with lists containing strings, integers or floating-point numbers. String variables are also called *character* or *alphanumeric variables* and can include alphabetic letters, numbers, and symbols such as a hashtag (#) or underscore (_).

Indentation & Spaces

Unlike other programming languages, Python uses **indentation** to group code statements, such as functions and loops, rather than keywords or punctuation to separate code blocks.

Example:

```
new_user = [
    66.00, #Daily Time Spent on Site
    48, #Age
```

24593.33, #Area Income
131.76, #Daily Internet Usage
1, #Male
1, #Country_ Albania
0, #Country_Algeria
]

Spaces, though, in expressions are ignored by the Python interpreter (i.e. 8+4=12 is the same as 8 + 4 = 12) but can be added for (human) clarity.

Arithmetic in Python

Commonly used arithmetical operators in Python are displayed in Table 18.

Operator	Explanation	Sample Input	Output
+	Addition	2 + 2	4
-	Subtraction	2 - 2	0
*	Multiplication	2 * 2	4
/	Division	5 / 2	2.5
%	Mod function (the remainder after division)	5 % 2	1
//	Floor division (removes the remainder after decimal point)	5 // 2	2
**	Exponent	2 ** 3	8

Table 18: Commonly used arithmetical operators in Python

Python adheres to the standard mathematical order of operations, such that multiplication or division, for example, is executed before addition or subtraction.

Example:
2 + 2 * 3
The output of this expression is 8 ((2 * 3) + 2)

As with standard arithmetic, parentheses can be added to modify the sequence of operations.

Example:
(2 + 2) * 3
The output of this expression is 12 (4 * 3)

Variable Assignment

In computer programming, the role of a variable is to store a data value in the computer's memory for later use. This enables earlier code to be referenced and manipulated by the Python interpreter calling that variable name. You can select any name for the variable granted it fits with the following rules:

- It contains only alpha-numeric characters and underscores (A-Z, 0-9, _)
- It starts with a letter or underscore and not a number
- It does not imitate a Python keyword such as "return"

In addition, variable names are case-sensitive, such that dataframe and Dataframe are considered two separate variables.

Variables are assigned in Python using the = operator.

Example:
dataset = 8

Python, though, does not support blank spaces between variable keywords and an underscore must be used to bridge variable keywords.

Example:
my_dataset = 8

The stored value (8) can now be referenced by calling the variable name my_dataset . Variables also have a "variable" nature, in that we can reassign the variable to a different value, such as:

Example:
my_dataset = 8 + 8
The value of the my_dataset is now 16.

It's important to note that the equals operator in Python does not serve the same function as equals in mathematics. In Python, the equals operator assigns variables but does not follow mathematical logic. If you wish to solve a mathematical equation in Python you can simply run the code without adding an equals operator.

Example:
2 + 2
Python will return 4 in this case.

If you want to confirm whether a mathematical relationship in Python is True or False, you can use == .

Example:
2 + 2 == 4
Python will return True in this case.

Importing Libraries
From web scraping to gaming applications, the possibilities of Python are dazzling but coding everything from scratch constitutes a difficult and time-consuming process. This is where libraries, as a collection of pre-written code and standardized routines, come into play. Rather than write scores

of code in order to plot a simple graph or scrape content from the web, you can use one line of code from a given library to execute a highly advanced function.

There is an extensive supply of free libraries available for web scraping, data visualization, data science, etc., and the most common libraries for machine learning are Scikit-learn, Pandas, and NumPy. The NumPy and Pandas libraries can be imported in one line of code, whereas for Scikit-learn, you'll need to specify individual algorithms or functions over multiple lines of code.

Example:

```
import numpy as np
import pandas as pd
from sklearn.neighbors import NearestNeighbors
```

Using the code above, you can call code commands from NumPy, Pandas, and Nearest Neighbors from Scikit-learn by calling np, pd, and NearestNeighbors in any section of your code below. You can find the import command for other Scikit-learn algorithms and different code libraries by referencing their documentation online.

Importing a Dataset

CSV datasets can be imported into your Python development environment as a Pandas dataframe (tabular dataset) from your host file using the Pandas command pd.read_csv(). Note that the host file name should be enclosed in single or double-quotes inside the parentheses.

You will also need to assign a variable to the dataset using the equals operator, which will allow you to call the dataset in other sections of your code. This means that anytime you call dataframe, for example, the Python interpreter recognizes you are directing the code to the dataset imported and stored using that variable name.

Example:

dataframe = pd.read_csv('~/Downloads/Melbourne_housing_FULL.csv')

The Print Function

The print() function is used to print a message within its parentheses and is one of the most used functions in Python. Given its uncomplicated utility—returning exactly what you want printed—it might not seem an important programming function or even necessary. But this is not true.

Firstly, print is useful for debugging (finding and fixing code errors). After making adjustments to a variable, for example, you can check the current value using the print function.

```
Input:  my_dataset = 8
my_dataset = 8 + 8
print(my_dataset)
Output:  16
```

Another common use case is to print non-processible information as a string. This means that the statement/string enclosed in the parentheses is directly printed by the machine and doesn't interact with other elements of the code. This feature is useful for adding context and clarity to your code by annotating aspects of the code—especially as code comments (#) don't show as an output.

Input: print ("Training Set Mean Absolute Error: %.2f" % mae_train)

Output: Training Set Mean Absolute Error: 27834.12

This print statement, for example, informs the end-user of what was processed by the Python interpreter to deliver that result. Without print("Test Set Mean Absolute Error: "), all we'd see is unlabeled numbers after the code has been executed.

Please note the string inside the parentheses must be wrapped with double-quote marks " " or single-quote marks ' '. A mixture of single and double-quote marks is invalid, such as starting with a single-quote mark and ending with double-quote marks. The print statement automatically removes the quote marks after you run the code. If you wish to include quote marks in the output, you can add single-quote marks inside double-quote marks as shown below:

Input: print("'Test Set Mean Absolute Error'")

Output: 'Test Set Mean Absolute Error'

Input: print("What's your name?")

Output: What's your name?

Indexing

Indexing is a method of selecting a single element from within a data type, such as a list or string. Each element in a data type is numerically indexed beginning at 0, and elements can be indexed by calling the index number inside square brackets.

Example:
my_string = "hello_world"
my_string[1]
Indexing returns the value **e** in this example.

Element:	h	e	l	l	o	_	w	o	r	l	d
Index:	0	1	2	3	4	5	6	7	8	9	10

Example:
my_list = [10, 20 , 30 , 40]
my_list[0]
Indexing returns the value **10** in this example.

Element:	10	20	30	40
Index:	0	1	2	3

Slicing

Rather than pull a single element from a collection of data, you can use slicing to grab a customized subsection of elements using a colon (:).

Example:
my_list = [10, 20, 30, 40]
my_list[:3]
Slicing, here, goes up to but does not include the element at index position 3, thereby returning the values **10**, **20**, and **30**.

Example:
my_list = [10, 20, 30, 40]
my_list[1:3]
Slicing, here, starts at 1 and goes up to but does not include the element at index position 3, thereby returning the values **20** and **30** in this example.